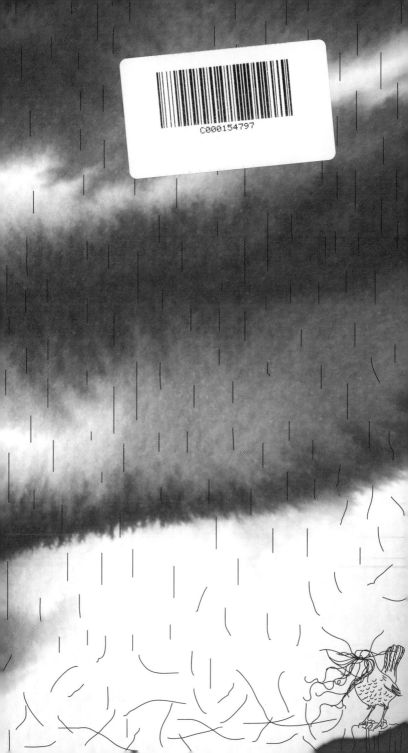

C000154797

Natural Artefacts
Nature, Repair,
Responsibility

MARION WALLER

CONTENTS

Introduction

BY MARION WALLER

The book *Natural artefacts* was published in 2016, when ecological restoration still seemed an emerging practice. Since that time, the words *adaptation, restoration, rewilding* have spread in the public debate and in the realm of public policies. Their urgency has become clearer, in particular following the death in 2022 of the philosopher and sociologist Bruno Latour, which has orphaned a generation of thinkers. Following his immense work, there is a responsibility to continue analysing our relationship with nature and imagining an ethical, political and sensitive framework for ecology.

What has changed since 2016? Ecology is no longer considered an incidental field of social sciences or politics. It has slowly become the center, but with an enormous need for texts, concepts, frameworks, clarifications. There are a thousand ways to consider ecology and its implications. This book insists on the need for an ecology of transformation. Behind the concept of *natural artefact* lies the idea that we should *get closer* to what is imprecisely called 'nature,' and not move away; that we should accept that we are *inside* and not an exterior power. Considering our productions as natural artefacts, whether restored ecosystems, buildings or, indeed, artworks, gives hope to delineate actions which are not necessarily destructive toward the environment, but can be both part of it and ethically active. This concept also helps us not to feel superior to other species, because animals can also produce their own natural artefacts, their homes, singularly and collectively, and because they also transform their environment. Remembering that all natural entities engage a transformative action toward their environment helps situate us as part of a global ecosystem and destiny.

The concept of *natural artefacts* calls for action and responsibility. The opposite approach would be one of a *frozen* nature, where human beings should not act anymore: this approach relies on a vision of a passive nature where human beings are the only active players. The only horizon then is to wait for defeat, collapse, or death. What if radical ecology was, instead, attentive to our urgent need for conciliation with the environment, with its knowledge and the possibility of acting in it? The degradation of the environment has advanced so far that we are all impelled to become healers, gardeners, doctors of damaged relations. This is why ecological restoration is so important: we all have a responsibility for acting on our immediate environment and for considering the long-term consequences of our choices. The new cartography of ecology as described by Bruno Latour, where one has to start by thinking about what (and who) one relies on to survive, must guide our approach. In a damaged world, choosing not to act, not to heal, not to transform, becomes de facto destruction.

This reflection applies both to wild and urban environments. In fact, among the dichotomies that the idea of natural artefacts attempts to overcome, the dichotomy of spaces is central. The diptych of wild spaces where human beings are considered as intrusive and cities where nature is considered as intrusive is becoming more and more obsolete. There is no space that has not been affected by human beings, first and foremost by climatic changes. And there are no spaces where nature is not centrally present. Hybridity becomes inevitable and necessary. In fact, in the few years since publication of the French edition of this book, the idea of adaptation has become more and more urgent, as cities face extreme temperatures. Giving space in cities to non-humans, both plants and animals, has arisen as an essential idea, while it was regarded previously as decorative or a detail in urban planning. Understanding the necessity of hybridity enriches our landscapes, our cities, our buildings, our streets, and creates new forms of beauty.

Natural artefacts remind us of the force of creation. While acting in the environment, creating forms and objects, we have a chance to reconnect with other natural entities, if we are guided by a valid knowledge of the environment and by ethical principles. Following the principles that this book tries to define, we can reconsider our connections with art, space planning, and of course ecological restoration. Healing and restoring the environment become universal actions. They can also become our major *commons* and the basis of a new political ecology.

Introduction

BY EMANUELE COCCIA

The most important revolutions are those made
in secret. No one notices, and yet, in the space
of a few hours, the world and its inhabitants are
no longer the same. They do not need spotlights,
projection screens or big audiences. They do not
need publicity. They do, however, require super-
human lucidity: because it is necessary to understand the origin of the movements, how the system works, and where action needs to be taken.
Sometimes all it takes is to replace a gear cog or a
line of code, and everything is transformed. This
book by Marion Waller embodies one such secret revolution in philosophy.

On the surface, it comes across as a study of an
object that is certainly important in discourse, but
certainly not decisive for metaphysics: how could
(or should) reflecting on the status of objects produced by *ecological restoration* call into question
the foundations of reality? Some small consideration starts to reveal the unsuspected importance
underlying this question. For example, the vast set
of interventions that aim to restore natural balanc-
es assimilated to spaces where humans have never
intervened is -in fact- very close to an even larger
group of artefacts. Just think of an English garden, in which the judicious choice of plant species
and their arrangement presupposes the perfect reproduction of an 'apparently natural' coexistence.
Now (we are led to ask) what is a *garden*? What is a
work of art that produces a totally natural object?
And conversely, how can nature, in the biological
and vital sense, be the object of what would seem
to be its opposite, namely *art*?

The answer given by this book is both simple and surprising. These 'hybrid entities such as reconstructed forests, reintroduced species, or even domesticated animals' are *natural artefacts*. They are altogether as artificial as works of art are, but also perfectly natural, as are all living things, including human beings.

The answer presupposes more than a paradox, for it involves thinking about how nature can be produced artificially. Seen from a distance, it would seem to involve the ecological translation of the question that has encumbered modern European art and aesthetics for centuries, that of 'sprezzatura,' whereby art, artifice and effort had to be able to produce (and reproduce) naturalness and spontaneity. Yet it would be impossible to confine it only to an exercise in translating old-school debates. Firstly, because this question is at the heart of any future ecological reflection: it is only by understanding the status given to these objects that it becomes possible to define what our relationship with other species might be on a daily basis. It is only by understanding what happens when we project or create a garden that tries to coincide as much as possible with the way species freely produce their interaction, that a new idea of life on the planet becomes possible.

From this perspective everything changes its appearance: which is why through a single, simple question, this book manages to provide a completely new idea of what it means to act, a totally surprising picture of the human being; and –also– an understanding of nature itself.

An action capable of producing what Waller calls a natural artefact is in fact something that destroys any possibility of distinction between *being* and *action*: if it is possible to artificially produce nature, then our essence, our identity is 'naturally' produced by what we do. *Being* is a kind of resonance of our actions, and ontology becomes a kind of theory of art that is capable of producing life and giving it form. Conversely, it is art itself that becomes something that seems to take place at the very heart of what we call nature: every single artefact we realise can wake the spirit of nature which is in the smallest portion of matter, in order to impress on it new forms. More generally, life is produced artificially, through a series of activities in which more than just one species participates.

The idea of the natural artefact allows and imposes two further important steps: on the one hand, there is no difference in the form and status of action between the agency of human beings and that of all living beings; on the other hand, the agency of all living beings is founded in the capacity to act beyond their own narrow, selfish interests. Whoever acts does not do so solely and exclusively following their own ends: this means that what we call nature is a plural construct, in which each is capable of chiseling, modifying, sculpting, and reforming the lives of others, improving them in the process. This is precisely why nature is so fragile and vulnerable: all artefacts can easily break, much more so artefacts that are built by more than one creator. The whole Earth, far from being an 'only' natural entity, naturally meant to host the life of all like a stage, is itself an immense artefact, the largest, the most important, the most difficult. Our planet is an artefact, naturally artificial, or artificially natural, and built by billions of individuals belonging to millions of different species from the different biological kingdoms. It is an immense tower of Babel that - contrary to the biblical myth - manages to draw the greatest solidity and strength from the diversity of languages, customs and forms. Everything we do contributes to the shape and survival of this enormous 'natural artefact.' Everything that every living thing does is an element of this immense and infinite act of natural world-building.

Ecology, then - far from being a secret longing for some sort of untouchable world in which no one has the right to act or modify the real, and everyone seems to emanate from a predetermined essence - becomes a huge alchemical laboratory, in which everything transforms everything and every living thing tries - through even the most absent-minded gesture - to invent and distill an alternative life for itself and all other species.

Avant-propos

Recent events such as the melting of the ice caps and the Fukushima disaster have led to a major awareness of the ecological emergency and the growing influence of the human race on the environment.

The concept of the Anthropocene has infiltrated public debate, reflecting the transition to an era in which the human species is seen as the principal force influencing the earth. While the facts are becoming increasingly visible and accepted, our theoretical approach to the environment is not necessarily becoming more enlightened and disciplined. At a time when everyone wants to become an actor in the ecological transition and act positively on their immediate and distant environment, a certain ethical and conceptual clarity is required. It is not a question of the philosopher supplanting or educating the gardener (or guardian), but of accepting that any desire to act on the environment needs to ask questions such as: To what extent can I intervene in natural ecosystems? Am I part of, or outside these ecosystems? Can anyone be a 'gardener?' Can I heal a wounded nature?

The extent of the ecological catastrophe can easily lead to a thought-malaise: the flow of images and stories of negative relations between humans and their environment can lead to the conclusion that any action of the human species in nature is a catastrophe, that cohabitation has become impossible. We are tempted to withdraw from natural spaces so as not to damage them anymore, to multiply the 'human-free zones,' to huddle in urban spaces where this malaise is expressed in a less frontal way.

This book starts from a concrete and extreme example of interaction between humans and the environment: the destruction of an ecosystem. Through various practices such as agriculture, chemistry, construction, or all the actions that lead to climate change, humans have indeed damaged or destroyed many ecosystems - forests, rivers, meadows, etc. Immediately or long afterwards, the same (or other) humans become aware of the damage and want to repair the mistakes of the past. They try to replant a forest, to reintroduce a species, to make a stream flow again.

All of these practices taken together constitute what we call 'ecological restoration.' *Restoration*, by implying strong human action on an ecosystem - and at the same time containing a desire to care for and repair it - raises questions about the acceptable level of human intervention in nature. Environmental awareness is paradoxical in that it encourages the withdrawal from nature at the same time as it makes human action indispensible to remedy certain ecological emergencies. For these reasons, ecological restoration has been the subject of much philosophical controversy, becoming one of the targets of criticism of human intervention in nature, which in its case would be disguised by a priori praiseworthy intentions.

Other hybrid natural entities incite criticism in the same way as ecological restoration: artificial forests, natural parks, urban nature areas, etc. What they have in common is that they are created by the human race, but resemble natural processes. These unidentified objects challenge the traditional hierarchy of 'naturalness' and blur the boundaries of the separation between human and nature, while for some, creating or modifying such objects is a crime. But are they not precisely opportunities to recreate links of care and responsibility between humans and their environment? By becoming involved in a natural entity to the point of being at its origin, humans have the possibility of reinventing their relationship with nature, of reinforcing their knowledge of and care for the environment.

This book sets out to name, delimit and define an ethical framework for the development of these hybrid entities: environmental philosophy cannot ignore these 'natural artefacts' at a time when untouched and unaffected nature no longer exists. Rather than serving as a repellent, natural artefacts must pave the way for a new conception of the environment[2] in which interactions between humans and the environment are encouraged around the principle of 're-inhabiting' the world, or gradually relearning to care for and exchange with one's surroundings.

Introduction
Weaving Nature

When asked 'are there unnatural things?' everyone is tempted to answer yes. When it comes to
designating them, however, the right words are
hard to find. The common noun that seems to
be the most opposed to nature is *artefact*; little
used, it reveals our difficulty to categorise and
name these things. An exercise, proposed by the
biologist Jacques Monod [1] and taken up by the
anthropologist Tim Ingold [2] , prompts us to reflect on the properties that are generally attributed to artefacts as opposed to natural objects:
how would extra-terrestrials wishing to verify
the existence of artefacts on Earth design their
detection machine? One possibility would be
to train the machine to detect regularity in objects, a quality that we spontaneously attribute
to artefacts. However, the machine would be
very likely to label a bird's wing as an artefact,
whereas it would classify bedsheets as natural objects. A second possibility would be to look at the
functionality of objects: unlike natural objects,
all artefacts seem to have a specific function. Yet
how could the machine distinguish between the
wings of an aeroplane and the wings of a bird,
which have similar functions, not least because
the first object was inspired by the second in a
biomimetic process? At this stage, the failure of
the aliens' machine seems to be explained by its
static analysis of objects: it studies the final product rather than the process that leads to it. The
aliens could then modify it in such a way that
it could see the complete history of the object

from its conception. It would then be possible for them to consider the genesis of the object, and to declare it artefactual when its form and function are produced by external forces, and living when its properties are derived from internal interactions. In other words, the machine would distinguish between objects that are made - artefacts - and those that develop - living entities. It is this genesis-based method that finally convinced Jacques Monod and is still one of the most common approaches to the artefact today.

When imagining the deployment of the machine on planet earth, it is clear that it will quickly be confronted with uncertain objects. When it reaches a bird's nest, it will immediately classify it as an artefact, considering that it does not develop according to its inherent inner forces, but according to the external actions of birds. We could then add an additional function to the machine: that of distinguishing between objects made spontaneously and those whose form has been thought out and planned by the creator. This criterion would distinguish the bird's nest from the human house. This view based on genesis and design contains two assumptions: firstly, a physical distinction meaning that each object has both a form and a material, and that it is this form that is imposed by the creator in the production of the artefact (whereas it develops naturally for the living entity), thereby assuming that only the form is cultural and that it does not mix with the material; secondly, a metaphysical separation between the human mind and nature, with the form of the artefact existing entirely in human thought before it exists in concrete form, the creative act being therefore only prelude to the evolution of the object.

Tim Ingold imagines another object capable of confusing the machine: a woven basket. The problem is not the form or function of the basket, but the process of its construction, which the machine now has the ability to trace. For Ingold, the machine could easily see this evolution as natural and not artefactual. Indeed, it manifests in the history of the object that weaving is the result of forces both internal and external to it, of an ongoing interaction between human action and the raw material. The extra-terrestrial machine could not conceive of weaving only as an act of making. This example of the basket leads Ingold to propose a paradigm inversion: rather than seeing the act of weaving as an act of doing, we must see every act of doing as an act of weaving. This new paradigm stems firstly from the impossibility of design: the amount of information required to mentally conceive an object in its entire form is inaccessible to the human mind. Thus, just as genetics cannot predict everything about the future development of a natural entity, the development of the artefact will owe at least as much to chance as to its creator: 'like genes, they set the parameters of the process, but do not prefigure the form.' [3] A woven basket develops in a way that cannot be fully predicted, as the properties of the material are directly implicated in its form. Returning to the example of the bird's nest, it becomes clear that the act of weaving is not restricted to humans: just like humans, birds apply a certain idea of form to the nest, interact with materials, care for them, and demonstrate dexterity.

The alien machine has therefore failed. Does this mean that it is impossible to define and identify artefacts? No. Rather, it seems that the common mistake has been to oppose the artefact to the living (or natural) object. This opposition, rendered obsolete by examples such as the bird's nest, has nevertheless continually shaped environmental thinking and practice. In particular, it is at the heart of debates on human intervention in nature, regularly seen by philosophers as a process of 'artefactualisation of nature.' Indeed, a certain cohort of thinkers, mostly American, has had some resonance in criticising the action of the human species in nature as necessarily harmful and as guilty of a 'great replacement' of nature by the artefact. These authors include Eric Katz, Thomas Birch, John Baird Callicott and Robert Elliot. They have been particularly vocal about human-made but nature-like entities: restored lands - rehabilitated after damage - zoos, animals raised in captivity, etc. Understanding these relatively overlooked entities is crucial for environmental philosophy. The question posed here is that of the creation of nature by the human species: what is the status of these objects whose genesis is human, but whose development can be similar to that of natural objects? The rebukes levelled at them by the authors cited above are of several kinds: firstly, they are generally considered to be artefacts, this category being regarded as proof of ontological and moral inferiority; secondly, they are seen as symbols of the relationship of domination between humans and nature, expressing the desire to keep nothing outside the *imperium*; finally, these objects are seen as forgeries by their implication that humans are capable of reproducing nature when in fact they are not.

Even though this radical view of human-made natural objects is not shared by all environmental theorists, it expresses a broader - and very widespread - view of the relationship between the human species and its environment, based on the idea that all human action in nature is anthropocentric and dominating. In other words, what humans do and produce in nature cannot be part of the continuity of ecosystems, and is inevitably supranatural.

Following Tim Ingold's theory that humans weave the objects they produce rather than make them, these entities appear in a new light: what is the difference between a nest created by birds and one created by humans using biomimetic techniques? Both seem to correspond to the common definition of artefacts, i.e. an object created for a certain reason and with a certain function. However, while the production of nests is a natural activity of birds, the human nest is a reproduction of a natural entity, made by a different agent in a different temporality, but capable of resembling the bird's nest identically. If the human weaves the nest, then it seems obliged to interact with natural materials and to confer some of the development of the nest to chance. This is especially true in a natural environment of hazards and risks; in other words, the human nest seems even more subject to chance than the woven basket. In this framework, the only, or at least the main, difference between the human and the bird's nest is the creative agent, and since humans are natural beings, their productions have the potential to be natural as well. There seems to be no justification for calling the human nest an artefact as opposed to a natural bird's nest: they have an identical status. Both entities are then in a theoretical vacuum; they cannot be called only an artefact - which would not be appropriate for the bird's nest - or only a natural object - which would not be appropriate for the human nest. Indeed, unlike these objects, natural entities are supposed to have no creator, but to arise from biological phenomena of reproduction. To fill this theoretical gap, this book introduces the notion of *natural artefact*. These objects are said to be intentionally created, but at the same time to be part of natural - not supranatural – processes; and to have the potential for autonomy. This definition will be explained later.

Ecological restoration inevitably creates natural artefacts, and in this respect it has crystallised the controversies on this subject as its practice has developed.

Restoration underpinned one of the main debates in environmental philosophy, especially in the United States, in the 1990s.[3] This debate was initiated by Eric Katz and Robert Elliot, who based their critique of natural artefacts on the example of restoration, accusing it of anthropocentric design, of justifying the destruction of value in nature, and of producing the illusion of the human species' ability to reproduce nature. Ecological restoration is therefore a perfect case study for insight into the issues raised by natural artefacts. Indeed, ecological restoration is unique in that humans, in recreating an ecosystem, are at the same time caring for it - in the same way as they would care for a sick person - and learning from it: increased knowledge of the old ecosystem is mandatory if we are to reproduce (and heal) it. This seemingly positive relationship leads to a reflection on the contribution of natural artefacts: restoration allows us to judge whether the creation of natural artefacts is good for both humans and nature. Can humans improve their relationship with nature when weaving new natural artefacts?

The distinctive character of natural artefacts - the fact that they are created - allows for a special relationship between humans and nature, and thus makes them interesting to study: their interest goes beyond merely having fewer properties than natural objects. By carrying out a process of creation, by 'making work,' humans are at the same time led to strengthen their bonds of care, knowledge and responsibility towards nature. In other words, the genesis of the natural artefact is its strength rather than its weakness. The natural artefact is an object spun in interaction with nature's materials. Its interest lies in being the result of mutual creativity.

The example of ecological restoration allows us to test this hypothesis and to draw conclusions about the philosophy of the environment as a whole: if natural artefacts are shown to reinforce human ethical aims towards nature and to benefit ecosystems, then there is every indication that humans are capable of non-anthropocentric actions in their midst, and that they benefit from being seen as part of nature, their intervention becoming an opportunity rather than - a priori - a threat.

I
natural
artefacts

1.
Natural Artefacts

Understanding what constitutes natural artefacts is necessary if we are to study situations such as ecological restoration. Since the opposition between artefacts and natural objects is not valid, it is necessary to fill the theoretical gap that encompasses hybrid entities such as reconstructed forests, reintroduced species, or even pets. The term *natural artefact* becomes necessary in this case. The recurrent criticism of hybrid entities arises from an ecological philosophy which I believe to be dangerous in its systematic exclusion of the human species from nature. Natural artefacts are border-objects that allow us to go beyond the classical oppositions of ecology; they are symbols of the necessary integration of hybrid objects into democracy. Rather than threats, natural artefacts should be seen as means to reconstitute a healthy relationship of care and responsibility between humans and nature.

What is an artefact?

In everyday language, the term artefact covers two notions: firstly, that of an object made by a human being; secondly, that of a non-intentional experimental result foreign to the object at study (e.g. sawdust or grass cuttings). It is also often used as a reference point in opposition to what is *natural*, confusing it with the term *artificial*. Thus, Aristotle already distinguished between natural objects and artefacts, contrasting those for which change is intrinsic with those whose changes are not due to their form or nature:

All the beings we have just named obviously present, in relation to beings which are not products of nature, a great difference; natural beings all bear in themselves a principle of movement or of rest [...]. On the contrary, a bed, a garment, or any other similar object has in itself, insofar as we relate it to each category of movement, and insofar as it is the product of art, no special tendency to change. They have this tendency only insofar as they are indirectly and accidentally either of stone or earth, or a compound of these two elements[4(b)].

The Latin origin of the term artefact indicates the action of making: artefact is related to the term artifex, which refers to craftsmanship, and to the bases factum (action, fact) and ars (composition, assembly). In English, the term appears in the form of artefact or artifact. In the philosophical context, it is generally accepted that an artefact is defined by two properties: being intentionally produced and being produced for a certain reason. Two recent definitions of an artefact highlight these properties: Ristop Hilpinen's definition of an artefact as 'an entity intentionally made or produced for a certain reason,'[5] and Gilles Kassel's definition of an artefact as 'a premeditated artificial entity intentionally produced and possessing an author.'[6]

These definitions lead to questions about the properties of artefacts: does every artefact have a predefined function? Can an artefact be separated from the function it has been given? Helena Siipi[7] offers examples to define the contours of artefacts: the chair and the newborn baby are both created by humans, but only the chair is an artefact because its properties are defined from the moment of its creation. A polluted land and a garden are both extensively modified by humans, but only the garden is an artefact because it was created by a human. Finally, not everything that is produced by humans is an artefact: friendship, for example, is indeed intentionally produced, but it does not carry with it the definition of properties or functions. It therefore seems more relevant to distinguish between artefact and non-artefact than between artefact and natural entity. Often the category of object is not enough: domestic animals and reconstructed forests may or may not be artefacts depending on the situation.

In summary, there are seven properties inherent in artefacts:

1. The artefact is the product of an intention.
2. The intention must be prior to the artefact.
3. The artefact has an author.
4. The artefact is produced for a reason.
5. The artefact is a functional entity.
6. The creation of an artefact is intrinsically linked to the intentional modification of its properties.
7. The attribution of properties to the artefact leads to new functions.

2.
The blurring of the boundary between artefact and natural object

The fallacy of seeing humans outside of nature

These seven properties define what an artefact is, but they do not mark the separation from the natural object, as the two categories are not mutually exclusive. In the modern world, characterised by the ability of technology to reproduce nature and the proliferation of hybrid objects, the distinction between natural and unnatural (or cultural) should not be taken as a clear separation; perhaps it should be eliminated altogether. The difference between artefact and non-artefact does not overlap with the distinction between natural and non-natural, but it is nevertheless interesting to consider the proposed differences between artefacts and natural objects. Beyond the normative distinctions drawn by authors such as Aristotle, some philosophers have attempted to draw a clear line. This boundary has never created consensus, mainly because of a confusion between the terms artefactual, unnatural and cultural. More generally, human action and humans themselves are sometimes considered unnatural, inevitably influencing the status of the artefact that is thought to be produced only by and for humans.

The philosophical study of artefacts is a way of crossing the boundary often drawn by environmentalist movements, as well as by certain philosophical movements, to prove that humans are outside nature, that all their actions disrupt a harmonious and fixed nature, and that their intervention in nature makes it impure. On the other hand, it is a matter of scientific rigour to recall the interdependence between humans and nature, the inclusion of the human species in the lineage of other species and the changes that have affected nature since time immemorial, caused in particular by the modification of the environment by all types of species. On this subject, the recent work by Roland Schaer[8] is enlightening: in order to reinvent care for the living and re-think the art of living - ecopoiesis - he insists on the need to consider ourselves 'within' nature. To this end, he reminds us that living beings have constantly modified their environment, sometimes by means of artefacts. Thus, the industrial age is the latest episode in the transformation of the habitat and not the first; it extends to the outside what was already taking place on the inside (energy metabolism in particular). Since living beings must constantly renew themselves, they practice 'continuous autopoiesis': they borrow energy from their environment, trade with it and with other species (including humans) and in this sense inhabit their environment. However, humans tend to forget that the modification of the environment is not unique to them and that it does not date back to the industrial revolution: for a long time, living beings have been building habitats outside the biological enclosure where they protect themselves from the hazards of the world, such as nests and burrows. Sometimes, it is in the very heart of the human being that living beings build their habitat: *parasitism*. This constructiveness of living things is at the heart of the 'niche construction theory,' which emphasises the modifying action of all living things and their interdependence in doing so. In the same way, agriculture and animal husbandry were not initiated by the human species. So-called 'social' insects, such as ants and aphids, have long had agricultural practices; for example, the attine ants of South America established gardens where they grew mushrooms long before humans did. As Schaer explains, observation of earthworms led Charles Darwin to understand that nature was more skilled than the human farmer, that the soil was the work of the worms, through which they built a habitat for others. If humans have enriched these practices with tools, it should not be forgotten that these tools are often extensions of preexisting functionalities in nature. Thus Schaer sees technical innovations as biomimetic prostheses, as metabolic expansions; machines pave the way for hybridisation, becoming augmented bodies. Certain philosophical rigours must be drawn from these facts: linking techniques to the behaviour of the living, recognising that culture is not the monopoly of the human species, that other living beings than humans modify their environment, that we are 'inside.' With these clarifications, Schaer invites us to be wary of traditional ecology, which is often tempted to consider the existence of an original harmony, as well as of positivist history, which tears humans away from nature and posits freedom as supranatural. The art of ecopoiesis is thus proposed as a new link between living beings: humans must join forces with other species to make the world more habitable for all living beings.

Questioning the inferiority of artefacts

Even allowing for salient differences between artefacts and natural objects, these do not justify treating the artefact as morally or ontologically inferior. For example, the distinction that artefacts are different from natural objects because they are dependent on humans rather than on nature is not valid, since humans are unquestionably part of nature. Similarly, the distinction between 'mind-dependent' and 'mind-independent', long favoured by philosophers, is no longer relevant, given the advances in technology. Thus, for example, certain "digital organisms" have acquired a capacity for mutation, competition and reproduction that gives them an independence and a capacity for change that is contrary to the idea of an artefact. Conversely, certain natural organisms, when modified by technology (for example, a rat in which electrodes have been implanted to direct its movements, or a human made up mainly of prostheses following an accident), are on the borderline between an artefact and a natural object, so that this distinction no longer seems relevant for describing and apprehending an entity. Moreover, as Helena Siipi explains, some objects - animals, plants - cannot be classified as artefacts or natural objects per se. In any case, artefacts, in all times and especially in the present time, are much 'richer' than they appear: firstly, they transcribe the intention of an author, of a mental activity, of a society, of conventions, and are therefore tools of knowledge and change. Secondly, artefacts make the world richer, bringing new possibilities, combinations and interactions between living beings. Finally, and perhaps most important in philosophical terms, artefacts, in that they are often derived from natural objects but require social institutions and the intention of a subject for their existence, transcend the boundaries between nature and culture, between the material and the social, the physical and the mental. It is therefore in this role of border-object, hybrid, transitional space, that it is interesting to study the artefact, and all the more so the natural artefact; in relation to a 'moment' that is the present time marked by the increased possibilities of technology.

3.
What is
a natural artefact?

It is increasingly clear that the common view that the artefact is the opposite of the natural object is not valid: the artefact/non-artefact distinction does not overlap with the natural/artificial distinction. The hybridisation of objects implies a rethinking of the scope of artefacts and their possibilities. The qualification of a natural entity as an artefact usually serves as a denunciation or denigration of the value of that natural entity. It is sometimes around the artefactuality or non-artefactuality of certain natural entities that thinkers have developed polemical theses. This is the case, for example, of Thomas Birch,[9] who denounced the fact that wilderness areas[10] become artefacts as soon as humans delimit them in space and subject them to laws. However, the qualification of a natural entity as an artefact should not be seen a priori as a negative sign. Even if this qualification has moral consequences, it should first be treated in ontological and descriptive terms before being treated in ethical terms.

It should always be borne in mind that the production of artefacts is a shared natural activity. Indeed, contrary to appearances, non-humans also produce artefacts. A dam built by a beaver, a piece of land ploughed by ants, a toothpick designed by a chimpanzee: they all meet the definition of artefacts. Yet no one would think of naming them as such, because they seem to be natural in contrast with the properties we attribute to artefacts. Thus, just as the natural/non-natural distinction is not appropriate for artefacts, the human/non-human distinction does not seem relevant either.

Natural artefacts in a theoretical vacuum

The term 'natural artefact' is very rare in philosophical literature, especially in French texts, where the issues related to it are very little discussed. The term 'living artefact' appears mainly in American and Scandinavian literature, in cognitive, anthropological and artistic studies, and sometimes in philosophical studies. [11] More often than not, the terms 'artefact' and 'natural' appear side by side to underline an antithesis: this is notably the case in the literature on ecological restoration. When the two terms are used together, it is usually to condemn the transformation of a natural entity by humans. However, certain hybrid entities such as restored nature areas, gardens, zoos, urban forests, cloned animals, etc., deserve to be studied in the light of this notion of natural artefact. This term covers the existence of entities which, by linking us to nature from the moment of their creation, allow us to reinvent our interactions with living beings and ecosystems, to attend to a nature sometimes damaged by ourselves, to reinforce our knowledge of natural mechanisms. This is not to say that natural artefacts are intrinsically good, but that they have a strong potential for knowledge and action in relation to nature. This statement is made in a particular context of the increasing power of technology, especially biotechnology, increasing our possibilities - to produce natural artefacts - as well as our responsibility - to repair nature. Yet these entities are situated in a damaging theoretical vacuum. It is therefore necessary to identify, describe and explicitly delimit these hybrids in order to better integrate them and improve our relationship with nature. The term 'natural artefact' seems more appropriate than "living artefact" insofar as it allows us to distinguish objects that follow a 'natural' (as opposed to supranatural) evolution, and thus allows us to exclude certain entities that are similar to nature, but express no continuity with it; whereas the term 'living artefact' does not allow us to make these distinctions.

The literature on natural artefacts such as ecological restoration often expresses a restrictive view of what nature would be: nature without human intervention, preserved, pure. Even if the thinkers in question - notably Thomas Birch, Eric Katz, Robert Elliot - recognise that the current ecological situation prevents any natural space from being truly free of human impact and that qualification as 'nature' is more a matter of degrees than of categories, for essentially normative reasons these authors expel many entities from nature without defining a new status for them. Thus, many entities find themselves classified as non-natural objects, artefacts, devoid of any value. Yet can a restored forest or a garden be reduced to the non-natural? For many human beings, these entities represent the only contact with nature. In order to 'repair' the dominating interplay between the human species and nature, should we not pay special attention to these transitional entities?

The philosophical problems posed by natural artefacts

Criticisms of natural artefacts can be divided into three categories:

1. Artefacts are inferior to other entities.
2. Artefacts cannot be natural.
3. Natural artefacts are inferior to natural objects.

In moral terms, artefacts are not 'problematic' for environmental philosophers as long as they are not mixed with nature: they are considered ontologically inferior and become a moral problem as soon as they are associated with ontologically superior entities that are natural entities. What seems disturbing, therefore, is the fact that one can mix, or confuse, an entity resulting from natural reproduction and an object shaped by humans.[12] Behind this first argument, we can in fact detect the problem of anthropocentrism: the natural entity, as soon as it is transformed for the good of humans (not just manufactured), becomes ontologically and morally inferior. This is, for example, John Baird Calicott's approach to domestic animals, for whom their status as living artefacts would preclude any moral consideration:

> Domestic animals are a human creation. They are living artefacts, but artefacts nonetheless, and are another mode of extension of human work into ecosystems. It is therefore deeply inconsistent to complain about the disruption of the natural behaviour of chickens and young calves on production farms. This would be much the same as talking about the natural behaviour of tables and chairs.[13]

Thus, for Calicott, the fact that domestic animals are transformed in such a way that they respond to human interests classifies them as objects. Eric Katz makes a similar point: 'technological products - artefacts - are thus fundamentally anthropocentric; by this I mean that their existence, purpose and meaning are all derived from the expectations of human agents, as individual persons or social institutions,'[14] or: 'artefacts are instruments or tools for the improvement of human life. They can only be understood as anthropocentric instruments.'[15] This argument of anthropocentrism assumes several prerequisites:

1. A human-designed artefact would only serve the interests of humans.
2. The human, although belonging to nature, when producing artefacts would then produce unnatural objects.

The assertion (1) assumes that human interests are incompatible with the so-called interests of 'nature,' of other living beings. This is a very strong statement about the functioning of nature. It assumes either that humans cannot intend to serve other interests, or that they cannot afford to do so. In other words, what is anthropogenic is necessarily anthropocentric. This assertion 1 is conditioned by the assertion 2, forming the following reasoning: humans, although natural beings, when they use technology to produce artefacts, make them objects that serve their interests, thus unnatural objects. Thus the idea that transpires through the writings of Katz and Calicott is that when humans use the medium of technology, they make their actions and what they produce *unnatural*. Yet the use of artefacts and the modification of the environment for one's own purposes are not activities reserved for humans. This would mean that a dam built by a beaver only serves the interests of beavers and is necessarily unnatural. This statement is neither intuitive nor logical. On the other hand, it seems obvious that a dam built by a beaver, or soil worked by earthworms, can also serve the interests of other non-human beings. If we assume that it is technique - or technology, often confused in the writings of environmentalists - that inevitably tips an entity into the artefactual, then how should we view transformed human bodies? Does a foetus modified in utero to prevent it from contracting a certain disease in fact become an artefact? As the philosopher Yeuk-Sze lo puts it: 'if a savannah repaired by technology is nothing more than an artefactual substitute for the real savannah, are people who recover after medical treatment nothing more than artefactual substitutes for real people?[16]

Anthropocentrism and the potential autonomy of natural artefacts

Eric Katz, through his arguments, expresses a certain vision of ecology which assumes that:

1. What humans produce is always morally inferior to what nature produces.
2. Human actions are always harmful to nature.

This pessimistic view supports the extraction of the human species from nature, suggesting that its harmonious integration into the ecosystem is impossible. Any interaction with nature seems reduced to the status of domination, never cooperation. By asserting the impossibility of the human species to serve interests other than its own, to improve ecosystems through technology, to produce artefacts morally acceptable to nature, Eric Katz effectively places all interactions between the human species and nature in a grey area. The only distinction that becomes valid is no longer that between living and non-living, but between artefacts and natural entities, the criterion of differentiation being only human intervention. It is indeed an exclusion that Katz pronounces with regard to them: 'these human-created entities have no place in environmental ethics because they are not natural entities.'[17] Natural artefacts are thus cast out of environmental ethics, without however inheriting a new classification: they suffer a theoretical vacuum.

Beyond these arguments about anthropocentrism emerges a broader Kantian view of artefacts: that moral subjects should be treated as ends-in-themselves, never as means. Indeed, in the background of Katz's critique appears the denunciation of the instrumentalisation of nature as an end: 'In contrast to natural entities, artefacts, as human instruments, are always a means to a certain human end.'[18] Katz thus asserts that :

1. Moral consideration follows from autonomy.
2. A natural entity manufactured or transformed by humans cannot be autonomous.

At this stage, it is useful to distinguish the state of autonomy from the possibility of autonomy. Indeed, in the same way that a human being can have a potential for autonomy without being autonomous - as in the case of a child or someone who is ill - we can consider that the same is true for natural entities. A restored natural area, a domesticated animal, can retain the potential for autonomy, even if they are deprived of it for several years. Yeuk-Sze lo proposes a distinction between 'possessing autonomy' and 'being autonomous': according to her, human impact may remove autonomy from a natural entity, but this does not prevent it from regaining it. This theory applies easily to natural entities transformed by humans at some point in their existence, less easily to entities made by them. Indeed, when an entity has been entirely shaped by a human and fabricated from scratch, can it claim autonomy if, later, in the course of its development, the human no longer takes care of it? Thus, does an artificial forest, a garden, have the capacity to gradually become autonomous?

Artefacts may deviate from their intended function, or the function may never be realised. The nature affected by humans can obviously regain a certain autonomy, if that is the goal. This potential for autonomy is linked to the possibilities of the modern period, characterised by the increased capacities of technology to imitate nature and to design modular entities. At the same time, the modern period challenges the notion of nature's autonomy insofar as many ecosystems are no longer in their original state and can be considered as 'sick.' Human intervention to repair some, to replace others, seems necessary, and may involve a temporary loss of autonomy. Similarly, so-called 'wilderness' areas often involve a very high level of human commitment to their conservation and cannot in this sense be described as truly autonomous. The point here is not to criticise the reference to the autonomy of nature per se, but to relate it to the current situation of damaged nature, which requires a new approach. In the same way that a sick person cannot be left without care on the pretext that his or her recovery implies the installation of artificial prostheses and a momentary loss of autonomy, nature, in its current state, justifies the proliferation of artefacts to assist it and help it to develop. It is therefore necessary to accept that new types of entities make the link between humans and nature and to give them a distinct status. Indeed, respect for nature in its current state implies giving it value, even if its autonomy is limited. It is not contradictory to defend natural artefacts while at the same time supporting the principle of nature's autonomy - including the human being. The natural artefact, if integrated into the ecosystem that receives it, is able to participate in the perpetuation of nature.

4.
The Artefact, an Instrument of Political Domination over Nature?

Beyond ethical considerations, the natural arte-fact poses political problems for philosophers. The hypothesis of the 'replacement' of wild na-ture by human-made nature inspires a fear of the extension of imperium, of the domination of certain individuals through the production of simulacra. This fear emerges in particular in the United States, where parallels are regularly drawn between the extermination of wilderness areas and the extermination of native Americans during colonisation. These themes had a strong echo in American civil society when Aldo Leo-pold's *Almanac of a Sand County* was published in 1949. This forester and environmentalist, de-scribing the natural surroundings of his farm in Wisconsin, criticised the attack on the wilderness as part of the national spirit: 'Should we now ex-terminate this thing that made us Americans? [19] The idea of the *wilderness* is a typically American problem that modifies the relationship to natu-ral artefacts and explains, among other things, why environmental movements and related phi-losophers emerged earlier and more copiously in the USA. The disappearance of the wilderness is seen in the United States as a symbol of the civilisation imposed on primitive peoples and nature alike. Some analyse it as the intention to leave nothing unchecked, while Aldo Leopold identifies this conquest and its conversion into economic use as one of the main criteria of civilisation. American environmental history has also been marked by the adoption of measures to protect the wilderness, in particular the *Wilderness Act* of 1964, which was intended to 'ensure that present and future generations of Americans will be able to benefit from the permanent resource of wilderness,'[20] and which provoked reactions from many thinkers, especially philosophers. Leopold was an early critic of the hyper-protection of certain areas as an excuse for the exploitation of others, of the American 'return to nature' and its excesses, which he summarised as follows: 'any protection of wildlife is doomed to failure, because to cherish, we need to see and stroke, and when enough people have seen and stroked, there is nothing left to cherish.[21] This specifically American context is essential to understand insofar as it has shaped the apprehension of natural artefacts, through two major assertions:

1. *Wilderness*, once it is governed by human laws and delimited, becomes an artefact.
2. Natural artefacts are instruments of power to tame the *wilderness*.

In both cases, the natural artefact - whether it represents a creation or a transformation - is seen as the opposite of *wilderness* and symbolises attempts to appropriate nature. This is particularly the view of Eric Katz: 'the creation of artefacts is central to the human project of dominating and subjugating the natural world. Artefacts allow humanity to control the forces of nature for

the betterment of human life.'[22] One represent-
ative of the critique of the American treatment
of the wilderness is Thomas H. Birch: for him,
the protection of the wilderness is an obvious
extension of a certain imperialist vision, including world's fairs, zoos, first-nation reserves, etc.
Birch sees the enhancement of *wilderness* as an
imprisonment in this line: nature is confined
rather than liberated, 'nature reserves are dou-
ble-locked rooms'[23] This is explained by the desire not to leave any self-determination to nature,
because such self-determination would amount
to the abdication of our imperialist power. Humans, under the pretext of protection and rights,
would thus impose on nature the integration of
an anthropocentric moral system. It would be a
matter of bringing our law to the 'savage,' as was
done for the Amerindians. Yet, for Birch, this
goes against the properties of wilderness, which
must be 'outlaw,' a space of alterity. He links this
analysis of the wilderness to that of the hyperreal,
of the simulation that characterises Western civilisation for some. Referring in particular to Jean
Baudrillard and French Theory, Birch explains
that only total control of simulacra is possible, because they are reproducible and interchangeable.
Power therefore prefers them to real and natural
entities, it creates its own world with simulations
of real things. The wilderness areas would thus
serve to simulate a semblance of wildness, essential to safeguard the meaning of the imperium.
In the face of these attempts at appropriation,
Birch recommends relearning to live within the
wilderness, to see it as a fissure, a 'counter-fiction'
within the factory of total domination.

In this context, the production of natural artefacts can be seen as an attempt to erase any 'real'

nature, the replacement of free entities with objects that can be controlled, modified and supported at any time. This semblance of nature would allow humans to forget that a non-anthropocentric nature ever existed.

Faced with these criticisms of domination and simulation, the perspective of an apolitical natural artefact does not seem to be a viable solution: the natural artefact, insofar as it involves a space to be conquered, replaced, filled, often affects more than one person and therefore needs to be shaped by democratic debates. Even if the constitution of a private garden does not require such arrangements; the natural artefact in most cases requires a 'dialogue' with surrounding entities, human and otherwise. Dialogue is a necessary step, as other species and ecosystems will be impacted by the arrival of the natural artefact. The designers of the natural artefact must think in terms of losses, gains and compensations with regard to other living beings. This democratic necessity is in line with the ideas expressed by the French philosopher Bruno Latour: 'the meticulous sorting of quasi-objects becomes possible not unofficially and surreptitiously, but officially and publicly,'[24] so that we can welcome these quasi-objects into our culture and assume their production. Natural artefacts, as hybrids, suffer from a lack of debate and identification; in this sense they also correspond to the practices of recent technology, for which Hans Jonas has recommended the establishment of an ethical framework and legislation. However, the successful development of a natural artefact is conditional on its acceptance by the local population that will be required to interact with it: decisions concerning it must be taken collectively. This ties in with the fourth guarantee of the 'non-modern constitution' proposed by Bruno Latour in the same book: 'the production of hybrids, by becoming explicit and collective, becomes the object of an enlarged democracy that regulates or slows down its pace.'

5.
Rethinking Oppositions in Ecological Philosophy.

The analysis of natural artefacts is part of a particular context of ecological thought and practice. It requires overcoming recurrent philosophical oppositions, notably that between biocentrism and anthropocentrism. Above all, it reveals a crucial need to integrate these hybrid objects into democracy.

Overcoming the dichotomy between biocentrism and anthropocentrism.

The study of the environment has undergone an important shift from an essentially scientific and legal conception to the birth of an environmental ethics. This birth implied the emergence of new objects and methods: it considered the non-human natural world as worthy of study and moral consideration independently of humans, introduced a new temporality (the future, with the effects of human action on future generations in particular), and widened the spatial field by taking into consideration entities of different sizes such as the ecological niche, the ecosystem and the biosphere. In terms of method, environmental ethics has made it possible to move from the isolation of the object being dealt with to a holistic approach that brings together systems and parts of the whole: humans and nature in particular. At the same time, environmental ethics has become part of political debates - mainly Anglo-Saxon - concerning the control of nature, wilderness, etc. It is therefore against the backdrop of this new environmental ethic, in which humans are brought closer to nature on the one hand, and nature gains in independence on the other, that the natural artefact must be studied.

The question of nature's independence is at the heart of the disputes between environmental movements, which are generally divided into anthropocentric and biocentric movements. Schematically, the former would study nature in terms of what it provides to humans in terms of resources and judge its moral worth in an instrumental way; the latter would recognise an intrinsic value to nature and judge it independently of its relationship to humans. The philosopher Arne Naess has distinguished superficial ecology from 'deep ecology', of which he is the main instigator. The separation is similar to the aforementioned schism between the biocentric and athropocentic ecologies. While the aim of surface ecology is to combat pollution and resource depletion in order to guarantee the health of developed populations, the principles of deep ecology defined by Naess are: biospheric egalitarianism, rejection of the image of the human-in-environment in favour of the relational image of the total field of view, promotion of principles of diversity and symbiosis, local autonomy[25].

These different views are reflected in the ways in which concrete environmental policies are conceived. They require going beyond the simple opposition between biocentric and anthropocentric ecology. The central issue, which is dealt with differently by various environmental movements, is the acceptance of human involvement in nature. Biocentrism and anthropocentrism do not offer a clear way out. On the one hand, biocentrists and deep ecologists tend to wish for a pristine nature, free of all human action, which they often consider negative; on the other hand, anthropocentrists, by defending the instrumentalisation of nature and human domination, separate the human species and nature by placing the former on a pedestal; human action in nature seems to be reduced to exploitation and domination. Thus, in both camps, the issue of human involvement in nature is complex and not very consensual.

This is a central issue because, as the name suggests, the natural artefact is always the product of both nature and human intention - in the case of the human-made artefact, at least, but not only. Thus, from one extreme of ecology to the other, there is no consensus on the merits of these natural artefacts: they are criticised for making nature impure by adding an extra human action, for being another avatar of our thirst for domination over nature, for reinforcing the simulacra present in society. Yet it seems obvious that the fight against artefacts as human creations inevitably leads to the exclusion of humans from nature.

Understanding hybridity

This intrinsic hybridity of artefacts is both exciting and essential. It is characteristic of a new relationship with nature, which some would describe as postmodern insofar as the classical separation between human and nature has been overcome. Hybridity is also at the heart of Bruno Latour's critique of modernity in his book *We Have Never Been Modern*. Latour hypothesises that hybridity - the mixing of nature and culture as practice - and purification - the ontological separation of the human from the non-human - have recently ceased to be distinct, whereas modernity implied that they should be considered differently. By focusing on hybridisation and purification at the same time, we have failed to be modern. Another central assumption of Latour's, which he calls the 'paradox of the moderns', is that the more one refrains from thinking about hybrids, the more possible their growth becomes; whereas the opposite situation was true of premoderns. Finally, Latour draws from this reflection on the proliferation of hybrids the need for changes in democracy, including 'non-humans'[26].

Natural artefacts clearly fall into this category of hybrids, and seem to have been little thought through by 'moderns'. They represent the interests of both humans and nature in a direct way.

Ecological restoration, on the other hand, seems to be an archetype of the hybrid 'quasi-object' described by Latour: 'everything gets blurred if quasi-objects mix different epochs, ontologies and genres.'[27] Restoration, by referring to an epoch, a place, while being artificially created by humans, makes its classification and integration into society confusing. In this regard, Latour's reflections on laboratories are illuminating: 'Boyle defines an even stranger artifact. He invents the laboratory in which artificial machines create phenomena from scratch. Although artificial, expensive, difficult to reproduce, and despite the small number of reliable and trained witnesses, these facts do indeed represent nature as it is.'[28] Is the same thing not also true of restoration? The process of restoration can indeed be entirely artificial and yet reproduce nature as it is.

Bruno Latour uses the term 'non-humans' for want of a better term, as he himself considers it 'not great.' For the author, it is a question of avoiding the dichotomy between nature and society, as well as that between subject and object. The term 'non-human' has the merit of underlining the links between humans and those on whom they depend for their existence.

Alongside the reflections of Bruno Latour, which have had a definite echo in environmental philosophy, the 1990s have been marked by the influence of so-called 'postmodern' thinkers, whose theories have major implications for natural artefacts. Indeed, even without an identified movement of postmodernists dealing with natural artefacts, there has been a widespread fear among environmentalists that these thinkers would advocate that 'all nature is artefact.' For environmentalist thinkers, this postmodernist view runs counter to the intrinsic value of nature and justifies all forms of abuse. A book published in 1995 gathers contributions from researchers from various disciplines to express concern about this postmodern vision of nature: *Reinventing Nature? Responses to Postmodern Deconstruction.*[29] The intention of the book is to respond to the 'postmodern deconstructionism' that would justify the exploitation of what little *wilderness* is left to the land: as summarised by Katherine Hayles, 'if nature is only a social and discursive construct, why fight to preserve it?'[30] The participants in the book thus attack the exaggeration of the role of cultural context in the approach to nature, the development of virtual reality spaces that purport to reproduce an idealised nature or the past of a place, the proliferation of artefacts such as plastic trees, that suggest that everything is a simulation, the emergence of a new ecology based on capitalism and competition (e.g. that Disneyland is as valuable as Yellowstone National Park), the obsession with change that suggests that all changes in nature are good, etc. One of the two coordinators of the book, Michael E. Soule[31] summarises these claims as follows: nature is under external (physical) assault as well as internal (ideological) assault. The second assault, the main tool of constructivism, justifies the first. Soule identifies a distortion between ambient postmodern discourse and the actual relationship of humans to nature, which is often premodern: while many humans are still pre-Darwinian, pre-Hellenistic or pre-Bernoullian, postmodernism allows for a disinhibited, deculpabilised relationship to nature, assuming that human intervention in nature is positive and self-evident. Thus, for Soule, the danger lies in this superposition between very diverse concrete relationships with nature and a postmodernism that tends to justify everything, so that humans no longer have the means to know what was originally artificial or natural.

Albert Borgmann, one of the contributors to the book, explains that the artificial has become the norm, erasing any difference between inside and outside, and worries that postmodernists are happy to see these boundaries disappear: there no longer seems to be any difference between a ski slope in the rocks and a skiorama such as *Ski Dubai*, an artificial snow slope erected in a shopping mall in the capital city of the United Arab Emirates. Yet Borgmann admits that the human impact on nature over the past several centuries has made it impossible to maintain a clear separation between the natural and the artificial, so he suggests a new scale of degrees: degrees of reality, rather than degrees of artificiality. Thus, while the mountain has a continuity with the surrounding world and the past, the skiorama is a discontinuous experience. The skiorama says nothing about the world in general, it is not part of the interdependence of nature. It is therefore in the hyperreal rather than the real. Borgmann defines the evaluation of the degree of reality as follows: what is eminently real has an imposing presence as well as a narrative and a strong continuity with its world.'[32] This new distinction is important in the moral evaluation of natural artefacts: while the measurement of the degree of artificiality is of little relevance to the study of, for example, a restoration project, its reality and thus its continuity with the immediate environment and the history of the place allow for some regulation of projects.

To this distinction between real and hyperreal, we need to add the distinction between the natural and the supranatural. In the same way that a real object is part of the continuity of real things, a natural object is part of natural processes as they have been shaped over millions of years. It is a question of establishing degrees of naturalness, often due to the way in which human technique is used. Thus, while a beaver dam is an artefact that can hardly be supranatural - because it is assumed that it will fit into the ecosystem without too much difficulty and will not provoke a fundamentally different development - a human-made artefact can be supranatural, thanks to the increased power of human technology. For example, some animal parks may be natural artefacts if their conditions replicate those of nature and allow the animals to develop in a similar way, while others offer only the possibility of supranatural development - such as the American Seaworld park, which has recently been the subject of controversy over its treatment of orcas, which are made to kill humans; a behaviour that is supernatural for their species. Artefacts produced by humans are therefore different from those produced by other species in that they may be natural or over-natural. Some of the human artefacts are in line with the laws of nature (by their internal form, their development, their integration into the ecosystem), so they can be called natural artefacts. This natural/supernatural distinction at the basis of the natural artefact is the synthesis of a vision of the human species within nature, which technique can sometimes place outside. Natural artefacts thus appear as a means of re-establishing a healthy relationship between humans and nature through technology.

6.
Identification and Evaluation of the Properties of Natural Artefacts

These different degrees and criteria of identification must be crossed in order to establish the properties which, if they are fulfilled, can constitute a natural artefact and distinguish it from a simple artefact:

1. The principle of autonomy: the natural artefact is created or transformed by humans with the intention of giving it a potential for autonomy and spontaneous interaction with other natural entities.
2. The reality principle: the natural artefact tends towards reality, through its continuity, its immediate environment and the rest of the world.
3. The principle of naturalness: the natural artefact is opposed to supernatural objects in that it follows the laws of nature (development and integration into the ecosystem).

Based on these three criteria, the term natural artefact already expresses a certain vision of what our relationship with nature should be; it does not cover all human acts that claim to be similar to nature.

A natural artefact can therefore be defined as follows:

A natural artefact is an intentionally created entity capable of being part of the continuity of natural processes and having the potential for autonomy.

II

ecological restoration

Ecological restoration implies a strong human involvement in an ecosystem, and in this way is a disruptive concept. The idea that humans can shape (*apply a design*) to an environment leads some thinkers to reject the term 'natural' for these restored environments. Restoration offers a framework for intensifying positive links between humans and their natural environments, and in this respect it may be more beneficial than a protected area closed to humans. Human intervention in nature is not in itself negative if the human species is recognised as being able to integrate with natural processes, including with technology. Restoration could thus be an example of the positive use of technology in nature, reinforcing the principle of responsibility rather than leaving it for future generations.

1.
What is
Eco-restoration?

A short history of ecological restoration

Ecological restoration is a nature-enhancement practice that emerged in the second half of the 20th century. It differs from conservation, preservation and protection. The specificity of restoration is that it aims to return a damaged ecosystem to a previous state. In this sense, restoration is in most cases a response to damage caused by humans, but not only - it is also possible to restore an ecosystem after a natural disaster. Restoration has historically developed in the United States, both in practice - eçological restoration - and in the body of science and thought associated with it - *restoration ecology*. It now exists on every continent and has become one of the most popular environmental practices, existing in a variety of forms and scales - from the eradication of invasive species to the creation of an entire ecosystem. The United Nations recognised the use of restoration ecology in the *Rio Declaration* (1992): 'States shall cooperate in a spirit of global partnership to conserve, protect and restore the health and integrity of the Earth's ecosystem.[33]

In the United States, restoration was made popular by Aldo Leopold, who experimented with it by replanting pines and restoring meadows near the Wisconsin River, and subsequently documented in his famous *Almanac of a Sand County*. Initially characterised by personal and voluntary initiatives, restoration gradually became more professional and involved larger and larger projects. In Europe, the Netherlands has seen the most significant restoration projects, notably the Oostvaardersplassen project, which consisted of reconstructing an ecosystem equivalent to those of the deltas of European rivers before their disturbance by humans, through the creation of a marsh and the reintroduction of ancient species. In France, the practice of restoration is little known and above all characterised by very little research, particularly in philosophy. The French debate on restoration is thus confined to professionals and focuses on technical aspects of technological engineering.[34]

In the United States, on the other hand, restoration has long been the subject of public debate and scientific positions. Following on from Aldo Leopold's work, a think tank was set up in 1987: *The Society for Ecological Restoration* (SER). This group plays a major role in the evolution of definitions and practices associated with restoration, notably by publishing manuals to inspire and motivate individuals and professionals throughout the world who wish to undertake a restoration project. In parallel, three scientific journals have emerged, linked to SER: *Restoration Ecology Journal* [35], *Ecological Restoration Journal* [36] and *Ecological Management and Restoration.*[37] The range of practices involved in restoration is also broad and subject to debate. The definition below provides a relevant sample:

The nuances of restoration

Definitions of restoration have evolved widely over time, in parallel with the advancement of thought. Here are three chronological examples given by the SER:

1. 1990: 'Ecological restoration is a process of intentional alteration of a site to establish a defined, indigenous and historic ecosystem.'[38]
2. 1995: 'Ecological restoration is a process of renewal and maintenance of ecosystem health.'[39]
3. 2002: 'Assisting the recovery of an ecosystem that has been degraded, damaged or destroyed.'[40]

These definitions give an overview of the nuances that can exist within the practice of restoration: the degree of human intervention (establishing an ecosystem or assisting it to change?), the purpose (healing? returning to a previous state?), the reference point (returning to a pre-human, 'native' state?), the methods (destroying to restore? reintroduce vanished entities or heal present ones?), etc.

> Ecological restoration is about reconstructing damaged ecosystems in their entirety, removing invasive species and weeds, reintroducing missing plants and animals to create a web of life, analysing the changes in historical conditions that led to the current condition, creating or rebuilding soils, removing hazardous substances, clearing roads, and bringing back natural processes such as fire and flooding to places that need these regular pulses. [41]

Restoration in the debates of environmental philosophy

It is not clear how restoration fits into the environmental trends defined in the first part of this book: although it may seem to be on the side of the anthropocentrists, insofar as it requires human intervention, the desire of some of its proponents to return to a pre-human ecosystem sometimes places it on the side of the biocentrists. 'Classic' environmental debates are therefore to be found among the restorationists. However, the philosophical oppositions concerning environmental protection are reflected by identifying with different practices: Frederick Turner identifies four trends in current ecology, namely conservationists, preservationists, res-

torationists and inventionists.[42] While conservationists would consider nature as a resource,
preservationists would favour nature stripped of
any human intervention, restorationists would
adopt an intermediate position by recognising
the intrinsic value of nature while seeing it as a
potential resource. Restorationists would defend
a dynamic and cultural view of nature: considering that landscapes have long been modified by
many species, from humans to termites, and by
natural phenomena such as volcanic eruptions,
they would not see the shaping of an ecosystem
by a group of humans as problematic. Creation-
ists, on the other hand, see value in the creation
of 'new nature,'[43] regardless of its links to a present or past ecosystem. Some of these may support
the restorationist view of reinventing a natural
area to repair it rather than rebuilding it as in the
past. Beyond these four movements, some thinkers or activists have become known for rejecting
any form of nature 'protection' as an extension of
human domination and a denial of the independence of eco-systems.

Within the practice of restoration, as in the practice of protection or conservation, three main
approaches prevail, with both practical and philosophical consequences:[44]

1. The *wilderness* approach, which aims to return
   to a pre-human nature, separate from culture
   (and therefore from agriculture), based on the
   intrinsic value of nature. This approach origi-
   nates mainly from the United States.
2. The *Arcadian ecology* approach, which favours
   semi-natural areas where human intervention
   is seen as positive, if it does not conflict with
   the conservation of the place. This approach

is lir ked to the proponents of 'stewardship', which promotes a caring and cooperative relationship between humans and nature. Restoration projects in this case emphasise 'cultural ecosystems', seen as part of European history. This approach is mainly present in the Netherlands, Germany and Great Britain.

3. The *functional* approach (also called nature development), which sees nature primarily as a resource and recommends restoration adapted to current land uses (e.g. agriculture). One of the policies of the functional approach is to reward farmers for producing or maintaining rare species on their land.

According to one or the other approach, the principle of 'good restoration' will not be the same. Some people will measure the success of a restoration project by the interaction with and acceptance by a local human community, while others will focus on restoring former ecosystems intact. Sometimes these two goals clash and the restoration manager is forced to prioritise. Two ideals clash here: the pastoral ideal of harmony between humans and nature and the primitive ideal of harmony before the arrival of the human species. The choice for one or the other approach is obviously shaped by the cultural traditions of the societies concerned: as we have already mentioned, wilderness is thus a typically American concern, while in Europe the cultural past - especially the industrial past - counts a lot in restoration projects. In some contexts, the choice of approach can be doomed to failure, as in the case of the forced conversion of agricultural land into wilderness in the Netherlands, where opposition to this wilderness approach forced the authorities to change course. In any case, it seems clear that the success of a restoration project does not only depend on ecological conditions, but also on socio-economic conditions. Certain moral dilemmas emerge from restoration projects: can a species be exterminated on the grounds that it is not part of the native ecosystem? Can you destroy an ecosystem if you promise to restore it later? Can a restored ecosystem compensate for the destruction of another ecosystem? Can we destroy the cultural history of a place or expropriate its inhabitants in favour of its original state?

Restoration at the heart of natural artefact issues

Restoration is often cited in debates about the artefactualisation of nature. In particular, the debate initiated by Katz and Elliot on restoration popularised the vision of nature being turned into an artefact under the pretext of valorisation. Indeed, since restoration generally provokes a spontaneously positive reaction - through the redemptive image of nature repaired, healed by humans - its philosophical critique has further devalued all natural artefacts. Siipi has shown that restoration is at the heart of the ambiguity of natural artefacts: depending on the context, a restoration project may or may not produce an artefact. For example, if a meadow was destroyed by a mining project, and all fauna and flora disappeared, the restoration of this fauna and flora consists in the production of an artefact because the entity is changed in its internal composition, function and even name (since the damaged area could no longer be called 'meadow'). Conversely, the restoration of a forest that was slightly damaged but remained a forest is not an example of a natural artefact for Siipi, as the ecosystem in question was not created by an author who would have attributed new functions.

The example of restoration is useful for us to observe that not all human intervention in nature can be considered as a systematic process of artefactualisation. Thus, the example of restoration is useful for observing that not every human intervention in nature can be considered a process of systematic artefactualisation. Often these interventions are small adjustments or repairs, which exist outside of human intervention: nature's inherent resilience processes allow it to recover to a previous state after certain events such as natural disasters. Once again, restoration as a natural artefact seems to be a biomimetic extension of processes already existing in non-human nature. The restoration projects in which there seems to be artefact production are therefore the most philosophically problematic: in these cases, following the definition of artefact that assumes the existence of a 'certain reason' in order to produce it, it becomes interesting to determine the intention of the author: 'he or she has - in general - an explicit reason to create an ecosystem of a certain type.'[45] The identification of this intention will allow - notably - to respond to the Kantian value critique: if a human decides to restore a place for the sake of their place and not just for their own sake, then the restored place seems to be worthy of moral consideration.

Restoration can be screened against the three criteria identified for natural artefacts:

1. The principle of reality: does the restored land tend towards reality, is it constructed in relation to the past of the place and its surroundings? Can it be related to a space that would not have known any intervention?
2. The principle of naturalness: does restoration allow the land to reintegrate into a normal path of nature, and not to become a functional ecosystem but outside the laws of nature?
3. In other words, can the restored ecosystem develop in an unpredictable way, deviating from the path predefined by human design, welcoming new species or losing some?

Indeed, the action at the heart of restoration is that of caring for a sick, damaged entity in the same way as one might a human being or a work of art - the parallel with aesthetic restoration has been at the heart of the critiques of ecological restoration. Secondly, restoration necessarily involves a process of damage that precedes it, in that it is the result of a sense of responsibility for the damage, of the need for compensation. In this sense, it embodies a new type of responsibility towards the environment, in line with the 'responsibility principle' proposed by Hans Jonas: the responsibility to repair. Thirdly, it is the symbol of environmental policies made necessary by a particular moment, that of the point of no return in the ecological balance, which makes human intervention necessary to mitigate its impact. In this respect, restoration, as it is currently practised, must be seen as an exceptional measure, even if it is part of the continuity of a natural movement of resilience in nature.

Restoration is thus not a natural artefact like any other and can contain very strong meanings for human-nature interactions. However, it seems to correspond to the definitions of natural artefact and thus proves the richness that these a priori ontologically and morally inferior entities can contain.

2.
The Critique
of Ecorestoration

The main philosophical criticisms of restoration are quite similar to those of natural artefacts and have often inspired them. These can be summarised in three main debates: the question of *design* - or the choice between genesis and quality; the debate on *human intervention* in nature - which involves the very possibility of restoring nature; and the controversy on *ecological compensation* - the link between compensation and responsibility.

Critics of restoration have sometimes tried to focus on the fact that restoration is a process of artefactualisation. The reasoning of these thinkers can be summarised as follows, based on the arguments outlined by Eric Katz:

1. Artefacts are ontologically dependent on humanity in contrast to natural entities.
2. Artefacts are inferior to natural entities.
3. The restored natural features are artefacts.
4. Wilderness features are natural features.
5. Restored natural entities are morally inferior to wild natural entities.

6. Human restoration of nature is the replacement of wild natural features with restored natural features.
7. The human restoration of nature is a replacement of something morally superior by something morally inferior.
8. Human restoration of nature reduces the total value of nature.
9. Human restoration of nature is therefore morally wrong.

This reasoning assumes several dichotomies: artefact/nature, wild/non-wild, independence/dependence on humanity; these dichotomies themselves establishing an ontological and moral hierarchy. The analysis of restoration thus allows us to answer the following questions: does dependence on humanity make one ontologically inferior? Are the restored entities both natural and artefactual? Does restoration consist of a replacement of a natural entity by an artefact of morally superior entities by morally inferior entities? Is the restoration of nature morally wrong?

These questions involve thinking about several aspects of restoration: the relevance of a judgement based on the genesis of the restored entity, the possibility of considering restoration as both artefactual and natural, the situation of weakness and care assumed by restoration, the moral evaluation of human intervention in a once-existing ecosystem. Beyond Katz's general reasoning from the inferiority of the artefact to the moral problem of restoration, human intervention is problematic in the following ways:

> When humans modify a natural area, they create an artefact, a product of human la-

bour and design. This restored natural area may look like a wild, unmodified natural system, but it is in fact a product of human thought, the result of human desire and interest.[46]

There are three criticisms here - design, false resemblance to nature, anthropocentrism - that deserve to be addressed.

The question of 'design': the choice between genesis and quality

Even before the publication of Eric Katz's articles that made restoration criticism famous, another American author, Robert Elliot, had made a name for himself in questioning the restoration process. In his article 'faking nature,'[47] Elliot challenges what he calls the 'restoration thesis,' which assumes that a restored space compensates for the lost value of the degraded space. Elliot builds his counter-argument around the comparison between natural restoration and artistic restoration. The study of this parallelism is essential to understanding the specificities of restoration. For Elliot, a restored nature is akin to a counterfeit, a fake: in the same way that a reproduced work of art loses value because it is not from the same author as the original, a restored nature is inevitably less valuable than an original. The importance of the genesis of the entity thus surpasses that of its appearance and internal form: the author, date and place of creation define its value and differentiate the original from a counterfeit even in the case of aesthetic similarity. Thus, even if a human reconstructs a landscape identically, the genesis of this new landscape reduces its value; its discontinuity with the past downgrades it. For Elliot, then, restoration is a deception: it feigns a similarity that is not, as in the case of a forgery sold as an original. Even if the aesthetic resemblance were perfect, Elliot argues that an expert eye could still distinguish the ecological mechanisms behind the restored nature, and that this fact alone would justify a difference in value. Two questions arise from this reasoning: first, can a natural restoration be compared to an aesthetic restoration? Secondly, what is the relevance of genesis for judging the restoration? Eric Katz has partially answered these questions in his article *The Big Lie: Human Restoration of Nature.*[48] In it he introduces the term 'design' to study artefacts such as restoration: he uses this term both to criticise Elliot's argument and to prove the inferiority of artefacts. Katz argues that Elliot's parallel between artistic and ecological restoration is dangerous: it suggests that natural entities, like artistic objects, have a designer at their origin. However, for Katz, the devaluation of restoration is not explained by a change of designer, but by the introduction of a designer into an ecosystem that originally had none. Indeed, this comparison with art would suggest that natural objects are all artefacts. However, for Katz, what differentiates nature from the artefact is the absence of design at its origin. It is from the absence of design that Katz deduces the independence and intrinsic non-function of nature. Conversely, restored entities lose moral consideration when they have a project and an author that precedes them. Thus, even if some natural entities do in fact perform functions (e.g. a mountain lion regulating the deer population), this was not intended in their design and therefore does not make them artefacts.

Does all restoration therefore presuppose design, and if so, does design prevent future autonomy and ponderability? A return to the origins of the term design is necessary. An article by Jacqueline Lichtenstein in the *Dictionnaire Des Intraduisibles*[49] sheds light on this problem. In it, she examines the Italian term *disegno* and its translations. *Disegno* was one of the major concepts of Renaissance art theory, meaning both drawing and project. In French, the two semantic fields united in disegno have been disjoined between the terms *dessein* and *dessin*. Although the term 'dessein' expressed the project, the gradual disappearance of the term 'dessin' led to disegno no longer having an equivalent in the French language. The English and German languages also use different words for drawing and intention. However, their association in a common term is significant when studying natural artefacts: it expresses a preconceived idea of the objects of nature, as explained by Giorgio Vasari:[50]

> Disegno is like the form (forma) or idea (idea) of all objects in nature, always original in its measurements. Whether it is the human body or that of animals, plants or buildings, sculpture or painting, one grasps the relationship of the whole to the parts, of the parts to each other and to the whole. From this apprehension (cognizione) a concept (concetto) is formed, a reason (giudizio), generated in the mind (mente) by the object, whose manual expression is called drawing (disegno). The latter is therefore the sensitive expression, the explicit formulation of a notion internal to the mind or mentally imagined by others and elaborated into an idea.

Part II

This definition of disegno changes somewhat the perspective propounded by Eric Katz. Indeed, it underlines the continuity that exists between the moment of sensory expression and that of the apprehension of the entity that aims to be produced. Disegno does not consist of a pure concept transformed into a concrete thing: it derives from the observation of the mechanisms of nature. Thus, if we admit that the human designs nature in the case of restoration, can we consider a restored nature as a drawing, as the manual realisation of a concept derived from observation? Indeed, Katz and Elliot seem to forget that if there is a discontinuity constituted by human action, at the same time restoration tries to rebuild a continuity with a past, damaged by disturbances outside the ecosystem. Restoration cannot be pure creation; its primary meaning is to recreate something that has already existed. But what differentiates it from an artistic reproduction, apart from the absence of a designer for the original entity, is precisely that it recreates a link that has disappeared: the reason for its production is the damage to the first entity, so it fills a gap. In this sense it cannot be seen as a simple counterfeit produced for pleasure or profit. To succeed in a restoration project, the author seems forced to draw heavily on the past, to show biomimicry. This is the idea behind another quote from Vasari:

> Disegno, when it has extracted from thought the invention of a thing, needs the hand, exercised by years of study, to render exactly what nature has created, with pen or point, coal, stone or any other means.

With this in mind, Yeuk-Sze lo prefers the term 'copy' to 'design.' Indeed, the copy inevitably refers to the original that exists in nature and reminds us that restoration cannot be a purely human concept. While the merit of design is to be new, the merit of copying is to resemble a past state - although, in the case of restoration, it seems of course difficult to return to the exact former state.

It seems obvious that original nature is preferable to a copy produced to resemble it identically; however, restoration refers to a particular situation which is that of *damaged nature*. The dilemma that arises, and in which Katz and Elliot seem to want to choose first solution, is whether to prefer a damaged nature that is not designed, or a repaired, designed nature. This is a question of establishing a hierarchy of priority between the genesis of an entity and its quality. The insistence on the question of genesis is based on a certain ideological view of nature above all: the biocentric position, which wants to minimise human intervention in nature. The anthropocentric genesis of a restored nature seems to be the main problem, as the relationship between humans and nature is seen through the prism of inherent dominance rather than potential cooperation.

The question of design is related to the question of the autonomy of artefacts mentioned in the first part: whereas Katz assumes that design prevents any autonomy of restored nature, lo opposes the notion of possessing autonomy. When a human conducts a restoration project, can he include in his planning a margin of autonomy for nature, a margin of unforeseen events? A first answer is that this margin of unforeseen events often happens unintentionally: the low success rates of restoration projects suggest the multiplicity of unanticipated reactions of nature. Holly Jones and Oswald Schmitz, for example, estimated that 35% of restoration projects are 'truly successful,' while 37% have mixed results and 28% are failures.[51] Scientific literature is hardly surprised by these mixed successes, knowing the complexity of the factors involved in restoration: landscape type, habitat type, hydrological regime, soil properties, invasive species, topography, etc. Thus, as Margaret Palmer puts it, 'we have little way of predicting the path that restored sites will follow, and no assurance that the goals pursued will be achieved.'[52] Despite the rapid development of restoration around the world, the lack of regulation, of shared scientific principles and the voluntary nature of many projects make it difficult to both succeed and evaluate projects. If restoration is so random, then it seems obvious that human design is only partial, and that nature has no trouble reclaiming its rights and freedoms. However, it is not a matter of rejoicing in failure as proof of autonomy, but rather of starting from this obvious freedom of nature and intentionally including it in human design. Thus, for example, it must be admitted that the reintroduction of a species may lead to the disappearance of other entities, and that not all future movements of the ecosystem can be predicted. It therefore seems difficult to argue that a restored entity remains entirely dependent on human technology: the reintroduction of wolves into a natural area will depend primarily on their biological capacities for survival, their interactions with other animals, etc.; the wolves will be at least as dependent on technology as on their host ecosystem.

Here we find the principle of autonomy defined for natural artefacts: restored nature is a natural artefact when it is created or transformed by humans with the intention of giving it a potential for autonomy and spontaneous interaction with other natural entities. The equation of restoration with design as constructed by the 'genesis theorists' Katz and Elliot is therefore flawed in that it overlooks the existence of an anteriority to the shaped object, the possibility of biomimicry in its design, and the capacity for autonomy and contingency in the object's development - in other words, not everything can be designed.

The paradox of human intervention: can we restore nature?

From the question of design follows the question of human intervention in nature. Although these two aspects may seem close, they do not contain the same basic problem: while design is disturbing in that it includes a preconceived project, human intervention is disturbing for the simple reason of anthropocentrism, the non-legitimacy of human modification of nature. Human intervention in nature seems to be the main problem point for anti-restorationists such as Katz and Elliot, linking to the broader issue of wilderness.

Let's start with the following paradox: a damaged natural area, which was home to wolves in its 'original' state, until the degradation of its ecosystem by humans. The authorities decide to reintroduce the wolves that used to populate the area, restoring the ecosystem to what it was ten years earlier. In its composition, the restored nature is now wilder than before, but the process that led to this state is less wild than the one that led to the state ten years ago. Here we are concerned with the dilemma of genesis and quality, but genesis is overtaken by the more general question of human presence. Indeed, in a restoration project, it is practically impossible to leave nature to itself after having rehabilitated it. A restoration project often extends over more than ten years, involving adjustments and constant monitoring. Nature is therefore in a sense put under guardianship. What seems to bother Katz in this process is not the human intention to repair nature, which he admits is often good, but the perception that it underlies. Eric Katz acknowledges that restoration stems from good intentions and a concern for reparation, but what it expresses is more serious: *the possibility that humans can make nature new again.* For Katz, this belief is pure arrogance and ignorance of natural mechanisms. He agrees with Elliot, for whom it is indeed possible to reproduce 'the same type of forest,' but not 'the same forest.[53] It is therefore the very possibility of restoration that is called into question. Katz uses Chris Maser's project in his book *The Redesigned Forest*[54] as a counterexample: Maser attempts to identify a method of planning nature, a kind of catalogue, which could even surpass nature. It is interesting to look at the thinking of Chris Maser, a former American forester, which goes far beyond Katz's critique of the cataloguing of nature. Indeed, before proposing restoration as a new paradigm for forest management, Maser strongly criticises the human design of the forest as practised in his time and points out the differences with the design of nature, of which the following are some examples

Nature has shaped forests in which all elements are neutral. We shape forests in which we perceive some elements as good, and others as bad.

Nature has shaped forests as flexible and timeless continuums of species. We shape forests as rigid, time-constrained monocultures.

Nature has shaped the forests of the Pacific Northwest to live between 500 and 1200 years. We are shaping forests that will hardly live 100 years.

Nature designed forests to be self-sustaining and self-regenerating. We are shaping forests that require more and more external additions: fertilizers, herbicides, pesticides[55].

Chris Maser therefore acknowledges the problems of rigidity, isolation, short-term thinking, lack of diversity, and dependence on humans in modern forest management. He attributes them mainly to a lack of knowledge of nature: whereas for a car or a human being there are catalogues, maintenance manuals, replacement parts and repairers, the knowledge of the forest is without any of these elements. It is therefore infinitely complex and cannot be managed in a way that benefits both humans and itself. For Maser, unlike a car or the human body, it is difficult to diagnose the state of a forest because the processes take place over decades and involve thousands of entities:

It is easier to send a person to the moon than to manage a hectare of forest. Sending a person to the moon is a black and white process: either you succeed or you fail. Managing a hectare of forest is a grey process. There are infinitely more parts and unknowns in a hectare of soil than in space[56].

Based on this observation, Maser recommends the creation of catalogues and repairers for forests. In his view, it is by building a '*sustainable forest* - thanks to the knowledge thereby gained - that we could benefit from *sustainable harvesting* - not the other way around.' Forestry as it is practised seems to him to lead inevitably to the destruction of the forest and the threat to future generations. Faced with this situation, Maser identifies a new paradigm for becoming 'employees of the future of the forest:[57] *restoration*. He even claims that restoration is the only acceptable type of forestry. Restoration is opposed to 'plantation management' in two main respects: first, it optimises the yield of the forest without altering its sustainability; second, it does not hide any costs for future generations, nor does it defer any damage. Thus, restoration makes the world more habitable for both the present and the future: any forestry that does not aim to understand the forest and restore it is not forestry.

Against the arguments of Katz and Elliot, Maser explains here that restoration can be seen as a counterpoint to the usual arrogance and anthropocentrism in nature management. By imposing greater knowledge of nature and leaving no hidden costs to future generations, restoration represents a new model of interaction with nature, beyond the simple care it provides. This does not mean, of course, that restoration should be the default systematic environmental practice.

Rather, restoration appears to be a transitional measure made necessary by a particular situation in nature. It is therefore not a practice universally necessary for nature, but - at the same time - it is not a supranatural practice. Restoration must be practised when nature cannot seem to observe a process of resilience without humans, which is not to say that the process of human restoration is necessarily inferior to the process of resilience without human intervention. As Frederick Turner put it: 'there must be places where humans have completely reinvented nature, just as there must be places where humans have given the initiative to other species.'[58]

It is therefore paradoxical that restoration is used by some authors as a model for denouncing human domination over nature, when it can offer a new paradigm for human-environment relations. One of the flaws in Katz and Elliot's reasoning is the confusion between anthropocentric and anthropogenic - in the same way that human genesis does not mean anthropocentric purpose: the assumption that all use of technology is necessarily anthropocentric cannot be taken as valid. The technology used to build a birdhouse may be anthropogenic, but not anthropocentric. It seems, therefore, that for Katz, inaction towards nature is non-anthropocentric, while action is always anthropocentric. Restoration is precisely a counterexample to these various arguments.

Restoration as a symbol of the necessary separation between wilderness and wildness

Restoration inevitably leads to the dilemma of wilderness. What is wilder: a space damaged but not shaped by humans or a space restored to its former 'wild' state by humans?

The American Wilderness Act of 1964 provided an official definition of wilderness:

> Wilderness, in contrast to areas where humans and their works dominate the landscape, is recognised as an area where the land and its community of life have not been altered by humans, where humans themselves see themselves as visitors and are only passing through.[59]

This definition therefore does not exclude humans from the wilderness but limits their presence to mere passage. However, when nature is damaged, this paradigm of wilderness seems more difficult to apply. It once again favours genesis over quality: can ecosystems be sacrificed just to leave them wild? In these cases, human intervention leads to a nature that is more faithful to its initial state, which is considered the state of wilderness. William Throop summarises the paradox of human intervention and wilderness as follows:

> If a restored member of a species can survive and develop in the same way as a wild member of the species, then it is as biologically autonomous as the wild member, despite the fact that its autonomy was restricted to a stage of restoration that involved human intervention and control.[60]

To overcome this paradox, and in particular to be able to think about restoration without focusing on the question of the "purity" of nature, the paradigm of wilderness must be replaced by that of wildness. These two terms have often been confused in American literature, even though they initially expressed very different ideas. The equation of wilderness with wildness has been one of the mechanisms by which ecological restoration has been condemned. To understand this distinction, we must go back to the founding authors of American ecology, notably Henry David Thoreau. One of the American author's most famous phrases was: 'in Wildness is the preservation of the world.'[61] By 'wildness' Thoreau did not mean the purity of nature to humans, but rather a positive quality present in biological life at various levels, central to the preservation of civilisation. In other words, he saw wildness as a catalyst for the creativity of nature, whose confrontation with cultural institutions revealed new possibilities and experiences: the nature-culture relationship was at the heart of the concept for him. In Aldo Leopold's work, the distinction between wilderness and wildness is more implicit, but the importance of interactions with the wild is equally emphasised:

> The wilderness has never been a raw, homogenous material. It has always been very diverse, and the resulting artefacts are also very diverse. The great diversity in the world's cultures reflects a corresponding diversity in the wilderness states that gave rise to them.[62]

Leopold was thus one of the first to put wilderness and human cultures into perspective, creating a space for wildness. His vision of wilderness as a valid form of 'land use' placed conservation and restoration within the larger project of preservation. Thus, he said, "You can conceive of a wilderness area that, if properly administered, can be walked through indefinitely and still be just as good."[63] From this return to the genesis of American ecology, we can see that wildness is a broader category than wilderness, including humans in their creative interactions with nature. The definition of wildness given by Robert l. Chapman's definition of wildness is worth remembering: 'wildness is a natural and qualitative source of infinite and adaptive metaphors, painting dynamic and unlimited relationships between nature and culture.'[64]

The emergence of a wildness different from wilderness results in the implantation of human culture within nature, without diminishing the value of nature. The implications for restoration are considerable: if natural value is inherent in wildness, and wildness, unlike wilderness, accommodates human impact, then restoration does not eliminate natural value. It establishes a kind of 'membership' with the non-human world and promotes reasoned human interaction that does not diminish the value of nature. For Robert I. Chapman, this approach does not lead to the justification of all restoration projects: it eliminates those whose sole interest is economic value, which cannot be included in wildness as an autonomous factor. A restoration project will only be legitimate if it reinforces the dynamic and unlimited interactions - to use Chapman's definition - between humans and nature.

3.
Ecological Restoration, a Practice at the Heart of the Jonassian State of the Future

The Responsibility Principle of Hans Jonas

The German philosopher Hans Jonas has had a profound impact on ecological thinking through his *Principle of Responsibility*[65] and other works, by laying the foundations for a new ethic in the face of the disproportionate technical power acquired by humans. In particular, he stresses the importance of a 'principle of responsibility' towards other living beings and future generations, the concern to maintain the conditions of a habitable world for all. Hans Jonas' thought has had a certain echo in civil society insofar as he represented one of the first philosophical transcriptions of the ecological emergency. Faced with the threat posed by each routine act of human beings, Jonas recommends founding a heuristic of fear: we must imagine the worst so that it never happens. For him, this necessarily involves limiting the power of technology. It is interesting to think about natural artefacts in this Jonasian context: if they do not represent a limitation of technology, they nevertheless seem to meet the major requirements posed by Jonas. Restored natural areas appear as entities corresponding to the ethics of the future, to the maximisation of our knowledge of nature and to the appropriation of technology as a care rather than a threat.

Hans Jonas' findings are as follows: we live in a distortion between our power to act and our knowledge of the consequences of our actions. This duality has made nature vulnerable, therefore engaging the question of responsibility. In Jonas' work, many links are drawn between the treatment of nature and medicine: this analogy is interesting in the context of restoration, which can be likened to medical treatment. Moreover, Jonas underlines the emergence of new 'spaces' made possible by technology, but not yet integrated into ethics. This is the case for certain medical practices such as cloning, but also for certain environmental practices of which restoration is a part. Indeed, if restoration allows us to repair nature, to compensate for our harmful acts, then environmental ethics must integrate it into its provisions. Restoration has major implications for environmental ethics insofar as it can mitigate certain actions, but also offer a justification for certain acts, which must be regulated. It seems clear that an approach to restoration that would allow any harm to an environment once it is restored does not fit into the framework of a Jonasian ethic. On the other hand, restoration, when it is seen not only as repair, but also as a means of learning about nature and of ecopoiesis for future generations, is interesting for the

Jonasian ethic and its imperative: 'act in such a way that the effects of your action are compatible with the permanence of authentically human life on earth.'[66]

Although Hans Jonas does not directly refer to the practice of ecological restoration, his work is strongly inspired by the concept of *Tikkun*, which comes from Jewish thought and means 'repairing the world.' Tikkun corresponds to one of the stages in the creation of the world, in which the original whole has to be put back together again after being shattered. This process is materialised by the restoration of the 'broken vessels,' which must be carried out by searching for the shards or 'sparks' of these vessels in the objects of nature. The Tikkun stage begins on the intra-divine plane and is continued by humans. Through their actions, humans can restore the universe and rid it of evil. This central concept in Jewish thought has inspired many thinkers, especially in the field of politics and justice, until its recent appropriation by radical thought. In the context of ecological restoration, the Tikkun takes on its full meaning in that humans draw from nature the resources for their repair: it then takes the place of the divine; its restoration enabling humanity to ensure its redemption. Hans Jonas' *responsibility principle* is directly embedded in this thinking, where the need to repair the ecological catastrophe takes on an explicitly sacred aspect and becomes a major step in the history of humanity.

Are ecological restoration and Jonasian ethics compatible?

Restoration, unlike other types of environmental management, excludes actions whose damage to future generations is unknown. Although no restoration project is entirely designed in advance, they are planned in such a way that they do not carry damage into the future - but rather eliminate damage from the past; in this sense they are 'transparent.' They therefore represent a new paradigm for human action in the environment, that of non-damage in the future, and in this way they respond to one of the threats of technology identified by Jonas: the separation of action and consequence. There is no certainty of success, but when restoration fails it merely stabilises a situation it would have liked to change. Thus, in the context of restoration, technique does not seem to represent a threat to the future. In this sense, this first aspect of restoration is compatible with the first principle of the ethics of the future, which consists in perfecting the knowledge of the consequences of our action. The second principle, that humans should develop knowledge of what is and is not appropriate towards nature, is also strengthened by restoration. Indeed, as Chris Maser has explained, restoration involves an increased knowledge, often unattainable in other settings, of the target ecosystem. Regardless of whether it involves dynamic or 'catalogue' knowledge, restoration forces humans to immerse themselves in the study of the ecosystem and to think about what is and is not right for that ecosystem. Indeed, humans cannot think solely in terms of the anthropocentric Good, since successful restoration requires that the properties of the ecosystem and the actions that will repair it be considered first.

Technique as used in restoration thus seems to correspond to Jonah's description of human power:

as the source of the feared misfortune, it is at the same time the only means of preventing it on occasion, because it requires precisely the unreserved mobilisation of the same knowledge from which the fatal power derives. By fighting the effect, we strengthen the cause.[67]

Although restoration - like other natural artefacts - represents a new form of incursion of technology into nature, it differs from other technical threats in that on the one hand it repairs bad consequences of technology, and on the other hand it brings humans closer to nature in the form of a positive interaction. Do these positive aspects of restoration justify a further incursion of technology into nature? Yes, if the act of restoration reinforces human responsibility towards nature. This rule can be valid for all natural artefacts. Indeed, the intrinsic property of natural artefacts - the fact that they are created - makes them primarily dependent on humans and thus creates in them a concern for care, a demand for perseverance and responsibility towards them. This is based on observations described by participants in restoration projects, as well as on the simple fact that humans generally care about a garden that they have created or a plant that they have planted. For example, Stephanie Mills, who describes the work of several volunteer teams in her book *In Service of the Wild* [68], says that restoration is of considerable importance to these volunteers:[69] 'People think that educating their children is important. People think making art is important. It's the same here. For a lot of people, it becomes more important than their job.'[70] Mills describes a natural desire to help injured natural entities, especially when one is in charge, in the same way that this feeling would unfold towards an injured human being. On the basis of these reflections, several authors have sought to underline the dominant paradigm of healing in restoration: restoration is first and foremost a care for the sick. This is the case, for example, of Donna Ladkin, who argues[71] that the healing of nature through restoration challenges the criticisms of philosophers such as Katz, who denigrate the possibility of a restoration detached from domination. Although healing may consist of manipulation, in restoration it seems mostly, and under certain rules, to be a matter of care for the good of the patient. While it may be argued that nature cannot choose whether it wants to be healed, unlike humans, it should be remembered that ailing humans who are not able to express a choice are still healed, as society feels a responsibility to them. The same kind of thinking mechanism should operate when land is damaged. As Stephanie Mills says, 'restoration is about accepting the fragility of things and investigating the emergent properties of healing.'[72] Donna Ladkin, drawing on Stephanie Mills' experience, therefore proposes two new terms for restoration to erase the sense of dominance that the word sometimes implies: 're-habiling' and 're-inhabiting'. For Mills, leaving nature to deteriorate on its own in the current situation is the same as leaving a sick person to die. It is our responsibility to facilitate nature's healing, even if this means sometimes removing some entities from the ecosystem, reintroducing others.

Accountability and compensation: the criterion of respect

If there is indeed a principle of responsibility for restoration, then we must first study its boundaries and potential abuses. Indeed, a 'restoration principle' could also be understood as the possibility of justifying environmentally damaging projects if restoration is possible. The ethics of restoration must therefore be able to draw a line between restoration as care and restoration as compensation. Benjamin Hale argues that remediation and restoration, contrary to common fears, do not remove the moral responsibility for environmentally harmful acts.[73] To this end, he introduces the concept of 'respect', which he argues is more important than harm. The question posed by Benjamin Hale sums up the new ethical problem posed by the possibilities of restoration: 'In other words, does technology change the way we think about responsibility?'[74] While restoration and remediation are not equivalent - remediation is a logic of counteraction, of cancellation, whereas restoration involves reproduction and recreation - they face the same ethical issues. For Hale, cases of environmental damage can be linked to inter-human situations: if one human puts poison in another's tea and then gives him a cure, the act of healing does not justify the act of poisoning.

For Hale, what matters is that there was a situation of disrespect: 'harm done to others is morally unacceptable because it is disrespectful.'[75] Similarly, if a human puts poison in one person's tea and gives the remedy to another poisoned person, his original act is not redeemed: thus companies offering to compensate for the damage of one eco-system by repairing another do not seem to correspond to the ethics of restoration. This issue is particularly important in the face of the proliferation of 'greenwashing' operations that justify the destruction of certain ecosystems by saving another, sometimes at the other end of the planet. 'Offsetting' mechanisms have even become institutionalised in several countries, making the damage done by private actors legal. However, such an act of disrespect, which is more serious than the damage done, cannot be compensated. Hale thus wishes to change the paradigm: to establish a moral responsibility based on the attitudes between agents rather than on the harm caused. This framework of thought allows restoration to constitute itself as an ethical practice while avoiding its drifts. Indeed, by separating the act of disrespect from its technological remedy, restoration is never used as a permissive act of disrespect - what some call the 'restoration thesis'. There can be no justification for any act of disrespect committed. This line of reasoning allows for a better understanding of the distinction between responsibility and respect. It also responds to the Jonasian wish to integrate new technological possibilities into ethics so that they do not become a threat. In this context, if restoration is not a compensation, then what might be the motivations leading humans to practice it? If restoration cannot compensate for an act of disrespect, is the author of the damage still the one who must repair it?

III

from

restoration

to

rehabilitation:

repairing our

links with

the

environment

Ecological restoration thus has an undeniable potential to make humans accountable to the environment and to future generations; it is even essential to repair the widespread damage already caused by humans. But there is no doubt that some restoration can lead to disaster, and that the possible 'range' of restoration is infinite. A framework of ethical criteria should therefore be used to analyse what makes a restoration good or bad, and by extension what can constitute a *good natural artefact*. A closer look at concrete cases of restoration reveals dilemmas that are often similar, both ethically and practically: questions of the degree of fidelity to nature, social acceptance - these two criteria are often opposed -, the choice of historical period of reference and finally the compensations accepted to justify a restoration. In the light of these criteria, the very term 'restoration' raises questions: should the reconstitution of an ecosystem not be oriented towards the future rather than the past, to which the word restoration necessarily refers? Replacing the restoration paradigm with that of *reinhabitation* allows the act of healing nature to be a starting point for relearning human-nature interactions, rather than the creation of a natural sanctuary. Reinhabitation sustainably inscribes humans into the ecosystem they are restoring and thus enables ecopoiesis; it implies a broad conception of restoration that goes far beyond ecological criteria alone.

Thus, a restoration process cannot be considered only as an ecological act: it must be eminently political. Reinhabitation is a political choice that implies appropriation by a community as a whole. It creates a new commons that the community will have to take care of and that will necessarily conflict with the interests of other actors. Decisions about a restoration project therefore ought to be taken after negotiation between all the natural entities involved.

Finally, what seemed to be the main characteristic of restoration - reference to the past - appears as a risk rather than a criterion for success. The obsession with returning to the past creates a risk of ecological cleansing and exclusion of the human history of a place. It expresses a static vision of ecosystems and is a cultural rather than an ecological choice. A good restoration is not measured by the degree of accuracy in reproducing a previous state, but by its capacity to be integrated into current ecosystems, by its sustainability and by its resilience.

1.
The Example of the Netherlands: the Dilemmas of Restoration

The Netherlands has been one of the breeding grounds for restoration in Europe. As early as 1975, the government launched a national ecological restoration programme, including the conversion of agricultural areas into pristine natural areas. A *National Ecological Network* was designed, with the aim of creating a 'nature infrastructure' of 750,000 hectares by 2020, which is more than 20% of the country's land surface. To do this, the Dutch state bought up land and forced farmers to move. However, this programme was implemented in a very top-down manner and without consultation with stakeholders, provoking farmers' revolt in the Gaasterland region. As a result of these protests, the Dutch state decided to involve the farmers in its strategy, providing for their presence in the 'new nature,' no longer conceiving of it only as virgin nature.

This touches on two crucial points of restoration: firstly, the involvement of citizens in the design of the project; secondly, the balance to be found between the purity of nature and the inclusion of humans allowing its acceptance. In the Netherlands, this second point has given rise to a controversy between two movements: on the one hand, the proponents of the 'nature development discourse,' and on the other, the conservationists. While the former - represented in particular by the World Wildlife Fund (WWF) - advocate the creation of completely pristine, pre-human nature areas, accepting compensation through intensive agriculture and the use of advanced technologies to bring their protected areas into existence, conservationists - represented in particular by the association Friends of the Earth - advocate a 'multifunctional' approach to nature, preferring less wild but socially accepted natural areas, 'democratic landscapes.' In the Netherlands, WWF's position can thus be seen as bi-ocentric, mainly concerned with the production of primitive nature by humans, without attachment to a particular local context. WWF accepted that some natural areas should be moved to make way for roads or industries, in order to finance primitive nature: the transfer of nature did not seem to be a problem as long as a 'superior' nature was promised in another place. Similarly, the position of nature development advocates towards agriculture is surprising: as they are intrinsically opposed to agriculture - considering it as unnatural - they prefer it to be as restricted as possible, and therefore favour intensive farming areas. This position, initially adopted by the state in conjunction with WWF, was seen as a betrayal of local history: citizens and farmers in particular saw the state as valuing nature more than their culture, justifying the abandonment of land that had been worked for hundreds of years to return it to its pristine state, which farmers perceived as a step backwards. The change in direction of the Dutch state - marked in particular by a shift in power from researchers to politicians - has conceded to the naysayers the maintenance of agricultural land and recreational areas in the new nature areas. In the end, the government's programme became more aesthetic and instrumental than solely serving the intrinsic value of nature as originally intended. This example illustrates the dilemma experienced by any authority undertaking a large-scale ecological restoration project: the choice between - on the one hand - a primitive and preserved nature isolated from its surroundings, and barely accepted by the local population and a nature still very much marked by human activities, but integrated into a local context, on the other. This distinction has been made explicit by Swart, Van der Windt and Keulartz[76]: they contrast the 'ecological development of nature' (autonomy of ecosystems, mono-functionality, little participation) and the 'societal development of nature' (lower ecological ambition, multifunctionality, more participation).

Secondly, the Netherlands offers a striking example of the difficulty of historical reference: while any restoration requires in principle a precise point of reference in the past, in the Netherlands there is hardly any 'original' nature left, as the landscapes have been intensively transformed. Faced with these so-called 'cultural' landscapes, it is very difficult to establish a new primitive nature, both for scientific reasons - prehistoric ecosystems are not necessarily known in detail - and for cultural reasons - primitive nature is difficult to assimilate in the collective imagination. The two movements therefore adopted different positions: while the supporters of nature development considered a return to a pre-human nature as non-negotiable (requiring in particular the reintroduction of wolves and aurochs), the conservationists wanted to refer to a historical and pastoral nature, based on the analysis of the successive transformations of the landscape by humans.

These initial elements make it possible to reflect on the criteria involved in constructing a good restoration: the degree of wilderness targeted, continuity with other ecosystems, historical reference, and the participation of the inhabitants. Based on these criteria, several authors have proposed models of 'good restoration,' sometimes involving changing the very word 'restoration.'

2.
Reinhabitation

The concept of *reinhabitation* marks a shift in emphasis in restoration: it necessarily includes a dynamic, forward-looking process and places the interactions between humans and the ecosystem at the heart of its success. This concept has been endorsed by Donna Ladkin and Stephanie Mills. Donna Ladkin's[77] intention was to critique Eric Katz's argument that restoration is always linked to domination. Donna Ladkin proposes four criteria for restoration to be conducted outside a logic of domination:

1. That humans see their role as co-creators working alongside nature.
2. That the aim of the restoration is to increase the health of the area and its biodiversity.
3. That there be a commitment to learn from the restored land.
4. That the projects of this land be taken into account.

This approach to reinhabitation or rehabilitation can be summarised in a general way as more collaborative and based on the dialogue between humans and nature. Indeed, the term 'restoration' and its inherent analogy with artistic restoration suggests a vertical organisation of restoration, with humans imposing their project, their design, on the land. However, any restoration project implies an increased knowledge of the targeted ecosystem and an anticipation of its mutations, and therefore cannot be seen as vertical. This new paradigm therefore insists that in restoration, nature is first and humans only assist in its healing, as Richard Sylvan expresses in his definition of rehabilitation:

> Rehabilitation can be seen as a cooperative partnership between the 'rehabilitators' and nature, in which nature is quite essential and does most of the 'real work.' Humans carefully contribute some of their own work aided by technology. This does not mean that they are responsible for the outcome of the process. [78]

If humans are seen essentially as 'sitting' with nature in rehabilitation, then the cultural-historical aspect of restoration seems to be called into question: it is about helping nature, not offering humans a space for environmental nostalgia set to their wishes.

Although the paradigms of rehabilitation and reinhabitation are similar, rehabilitation emphasises the pre-eminent role of nature while reinhabitation focuses on the efforts that must be made by humans to understand an ecosystem and learn to live in harmony with it. For the proponents of rehabilitation, what a human learns from a restoration project is at least as important as the care given to nature. This is at the heart of the principle of natural artefacts: the involvement of humans in their production allows at the same time an unprecedented rapprochement of humans and nature, through positive interactions of care and learning. In this respect, the shift from restoration to reinhabitation seems to be of great significance for the analysis of the contribution of natural artefacts: it underlines the re-learning of respectful living towards the environment, of belonging to a natural community that includes humans and to a particular local ecosystem. Stephanie Mills' definition of reinhabitation highlights all these points:

> Reinhabitation means living-in, in an area that has been disturbed and injured by past exploitation. It means becoming aware of the ecological links that operate in and around this area. It also involves understanding the evolving social activities and behaviours that will enrich the life of that place, restore its life systems, and establish an ecologically and socially sustainable pattern of existence. In short, it involves becoming fully alive *with* and *in* a place. It involves candidacy to be a member of a biotic community, and an end to being its exploiter.[79]

In this context, restoration becomes a practice at the heart of a wider system of interactions with nature, integrated into a process of knowledge of the ecosystem, starting from its practice and continuing independently. This approach is in line with the principle of 'ecopoiesis' proposed by Roland Schaer, whose aim is to *make the world more habitable*. The natural artefact then becomes one of the crucial tools for a new framework of exchange with the environment; in the case of restoration, the natural artefact is often even the origin of this new framework. Indeed, since restoration involves a process of in-depth study of the ecosystem, the knowledge gained from it can be reused in other environmental actions, whatever their nature. Thus, as Stephanie Mills explains, reinhabitation is part of a continuum of other human-nature interactions - what she calls 'elegant construction techniques,' which it both learns from and can augment:

> Reinhabitation involves learning the full history of a bioregion or river, and developing a vision of a sustainable ecological community from this knowledge and from what we have learned in the last half century about elegant building, gardening, recycling, energy conservation and waste treatment techniques.[80]

What are the practical consequences of this move towards reinhabitation? Firstly, whereas restoration implies a strong fidelity to the original entity, reinhabitation is content with similarity and similar species. Secondly, whereas restoration tends to make the restored place a sanctuary, or at least to restrict access to it, reinhabitation necessarily implies reinvesting in the ecosystem, learning to live in it and to have 'economic exchanges' there, not in a touristic manner, but in order to engage in economic and material exchanges with the milieu. Thus, for Stephanie Mills, this economic aspect represents one of the main differences between restoration and reinhabitation, as restoration fails to move away from the traditional system of a sanctified nature becoming a commodity: 'restoration does not create alternatives to the socio-economic system that makes restoration necessary; whereas reinhabitation does.'[81] Finally, one of the major differences of reinhabitation is that it favours a dynamic vision of the ecosystem over the idyllic, static vision of the ecosystem, i.e. it directs restoration towards the future rather than the past.

These elements complement the four principles proposed by Donna Ladkin to ensure that restoration is not linked to domination:

1. That humans see their role as facilitators and co-creators working alongside nature: this principle stems from the paradox that most natural environments today need humans to remain natural, and that it is the responsibility of humans to heal sick ecosystems.
2. That there is a commitment to learning from the restored land: it is about looking at what happens, rather than what should happen.
3. That the projects of this land are taken into account: this means not considering the land as passive but as an independent agent with its own projects, with which it is appropriate to negotiate.

Indeed, restoration has a strong potential to initiate 'negotiation' relationships between humans and nature, and to prevent domination at the same time. The idea of negotiation is crucial in the paradigm of *humans-in-nature*: it allows nature to be seen as a space of interaction and exchange between several entities seen as 'actors' with 'interests.' The sociologist Matthias Gross[82] studied restoration in the light of the systems of thought of Emile Durkheim and Georg Simmel: he generated the idea that ecological restoration is a practice that fits in with Georg Simmel's vision of society as a network, with the particularity of integrating non-humans. He sees restoration as a transaction that (ideally) involves the members of an entire community, beyond the elite, and more generally the members of an entire ecosystem. For him, nature becomes an actor insofar as it has developments that cannot be predicted, and can 'refuse' human action if it is not in line with its history and internal shape. Matthias Gross concludes as follows: "In ecological restoration, society negotiates with nature, seen not only as a subject of research, but more as an actor. [83] This conclusion supports the idea that natural artefacts can constitute new intermediary objects between humans and nature, at the same time being tools for rapprochement and agents of change.

3.
The Necessity for Supra-ecological Restoration

Expanding the scope of restoration ecology

One of the criticisms traditionally made of restoration is that it is limited to strictly ecological issues, whereas its success is conditioned by much broader criteria, as the example of the Netherlands has shown. The philosopher Eric Higgs was one of the first to criticise this flaw in restoration, both in his practice and in his academic study: he calls it the 'two-culture problem.' Restoration project leaders find themselves in a complicated context of negotiation between science and other disciplines on the one hand, and between professionals and laypersons on the other.

It follows that, while the first restoration projects were often carried out by specialised scientists, the thousands of volunteers now involved throughout the world have no framework of thought and no reference value. Eric Higgs denounces the fact that restoration ecology - the set of scientific practices that make up the discipline - has remained confined to a limited number of disciplines, making it impossible to carry out 'good restoration.' For Higgs, experience has shown that amateurs can do restoration as well as professionals, with success depending above all on a single criterion based on understanding and anchoring in a place, a criterion that Aldo Leopold had already identified in the early days of restoration. Higgs therefore considers that the moral criterion of anchoring in a place is the solution to the gaps between amateur and professional practices:

> My antidote to the two-culture problem is to ensure that those who tend to be restorationists understand the moral core of their work, which is rooted in a passionate understanding of a place.[84]

An inclusive framework for ecological restoration

An inclusive framework for ecological restoration beyond these disciplinary aspects, the practice of restoration must also go well beyond ecology to be successful: any restoration must be doubly beneficial - to nature and to the human community. Eric Higgs has advocated a vision of 'eco-cultural restoration':[85] for him, any restoration must be extended to include political, social, aesthetic and moral aspects. Thus, it is not enough for a restoration to be ecologically efficient to be a good restoration. Higgs himself was inspired by John Cairns, who proposed an 'eco-social' restoration:

> Because of its interdisciplinary nature, ecological restoration must involve eco-social restoration. This is a process of re-examining the relationship between human societies and natural systems, so that destruction and repair offset each other and perhaps restoration practices ultimately outweigh destruction practices.[86]

Cairns thus called for the recognition of mutual interests between restoration practitioners and the public, and the recognition of the equal importance of the human and technological aims. In this he laid the foundations for future 'rehab'.

Eric Higgs also considers ecological aspects to be as important as any other, because for him the success of a restoration depends on negotiation with all the actors involved; it therefore depends as much on the final ecosystem as on the process that led to it. He asserts the need to centre negotiations around endpoints that must be determined in advance: what land area? What historical state should be targeted? What technical means? What cultural practices should be maintained - agriculture, fires, etc.? These reference points cannot be decided by professionals or authorities alone; the restorationist must respond to the pastoral image of mediating between the imperatives of nature and culture.

In order to develop the most inclusive framework possible, Eric Higgs recommends that restorationists follow a three-step nesting approach: firstly, a restoration must be *effective* - i.e. ecologically effective -; which is a necessary condition for it to be *efficient* ('an efficient restoration is an effective restoration accomplished in the shortest possible time, with the least possible input of labour, resources and materials' [87]); and finally, it must be *extensive*, i.e. eco-social. At the same time, Higgs identifies three principles of ecosystem fidelity that must be followed: structural and compositional replication, functional success and sustainability. Following these three principles can lead to a difference from a so-called 'classical' restoration that would like to see the pure reproduction of the past, insofar as on the one hand functional success sometimes implies permanent human action - such as setting fires to maintain grasslands -, and on the other hand the sustainability of an ecosystem obliges one to think about the future of this ecosystem, which often requires an internal form different from its past, given the changes that have occurred in the environment in general.

Thus, it is not enough for a restoration to be efficient or effective for it to be a good restoration; its framework must necessarily be more inclusive and go beyond ecology alone.

The necessary political dimension of restoration

The political dimension is not contingent in the restoration process: it is a condition for success. For 'good restoration' to take place, i.e. resto-

ration that promotes increased interactions between a human community and a natural ecosystem, it must be at the heart of a democratic
and collaborative process. If one were to deny the
political aspect of restoration, then a restoration
carried out by forced labour would be of equal
value to a restoration carried out by volunteers
from a local community. However, it is necessary to consider the latter restoration as better
than the former, at the same ecological level, and
to evaluate any restoration by forced labour as a
'bad restoration.' Thus, restoration cannot be a
politically neutral practice, it cannot be adapted
to all regimes; the non-recognition of its political
character would prevent its instrumentalisation
from being denounced.

Among the relationships between humans and
nature that can generally be described as political, restoration appears to have a particular political dimension, characterised by its inherent
democratic potential. Indeed, by comparing
preservation and restoration, both of which are
political activities - in that they involve a public
choice to act or not to act on a piece of land, to
change its assignment - we notice that whereas
in preservation there is no value produced, restorationists are engaged in a collective process
of value creation. This process creates value for
both nature and the human community; it does
so if restoration is carried out through democratic and egalitarian choices, involving the widest
possible participation. There is a debate among
restoration philosophers: while William Jordan
III[88] characterises restoration as inherently democratic, Eric Higgs and Andrew Light[89] prefer to
see an inherent democratic potential. William
Jordan III argues that all restoration is democrat-

ic because it necessarily involves local negotiation and community ownership of nature. For Light and Higgs, the democratic potential of restoration is strong, but it is not fulfilled in many projects, especially in what they call 'corporate sponsored ecological restorations' which have been growing in the US since the 1990s.[90] These restorations are used by large companies to improve their environmental image, they are carried out by employees within a hierarchical framework, and the location of the restorations is of lesser importance to the companies - it would make no difference to the company if they were to take place elsewhere. For all these reasons, Light and Higgs see them as commodifications of nature and as bad restorations because neither their method nor their purpose is democratic, and because they do not establish a link between a human community and the surrounding nature, which is the unique value of restoration. The risk of greenwashing is therefore high when companies are interested in restoration as a communication or compensation tool. For Light and Higgs, the alternative that enhances the democratic potential of restoration is localism: the democratic potential is then realised in new local relationships between humans and nature. Indeed, in a restoration marked by localism, the dialogue between humans and between humans and nature will have to be equivalent to the exchanges traditionally conducted in a democratic society. But this potential cannot be realised on its own: it is the result of a political context created in such a way that the common opinion considers a good restoration as a democratic restoration. In this, it is the responsibility of those who influence this political context to encourage opinion to go beyond the purely technical aspects of restoration and to consider its inclusive framework.

Who should carry out a restoration?

This political dimension raises the question of *who* can effect a restoration. A clear shift has taken place in restoration circles as the practice has developed around the world: whereas the majority of projects were previously run by volunteers, the professionalisation of restoration has gradually intervened, changing its modalities. Does professional restoration, operated by a specialised company, have similar democratic potential to that of community-based restoration? Andrew Light has addressed this question[91] and identifies a risk that the practices associated with professionalisation - the certification of volunteers, accreditation of curricula, regulation of projects, etc. - threaten to degrade the democratic potential of a community-based catering service. For him, restoration must preserve the ideal that public participation in a public activity increases its value. At the same time, Andrew Light admits that all-volunteer restoration projects, such as the Chicago Wilderness Project, run the risk of not being able to be defended in public debate because no expert can certify them, and restoration is then formally defined only by its opponents. For Light, what matters is not so much who carries out the restoration, but rather who decides on it: he thus proposes the enactment of a law according to which, when public money is committed to a restoration project, local communities have the power to refuse or accept a restoration, and in the latter case the accredited money is used to employ experts to accompany the work of the volunteers. Thus, 'good restoration' must necessarily involve democratic interactions within a community and in its relationship to nature. This political dimension is necessary for the desired goal of any restoration project to 're-inhabit nature.'

It is therefore difficult to determine the extent of the people who should be consulted during a restoration: beyond the necessary consultation of the local community surrounding the restoration site, the national scope of certain natural sites suggests that the consultation can be much broader. It is striking that the historical inhabitants of a place are often forgotten: while one wishes to restore an ecosystem to its state existing at the time of another population, the only people included in the process are often the current inhabitants of the land, with little interest given to the descendants of the primary communities. This is the paradox expressed by Stuart K. Allison when discussing the case of North American restorations:

> There is a sad irony in restoring North American ecosystems to their native American state, without even consulting or including native Americans in the restoration process.[92]

It therefore seems just as important to judge who can decide on restoration as who can carry it out. In order for a restoration not only to serve the interests of its author, it is indeed a whole community that must be consulted, and which through consultation will reflect on its links with nature, regardless of whether it carries out the restoration or not.

4.
The Temporal Paradox of Restoration: The Impossible Return to the Past

Despite the technological and biomimetic advances that make it possible to restore an ecosystem to a previous state, a doubt remains: is it really relevant to return nature to its past state? Does this not go against all logic and a dynamic vision of ecosystems? Is it respectful of nature to set it back hundreds or thousands of years? Some counter-thoughts have emerged recently, seeing the retrospectivity of restoration as its main flaw. Indeed, past ecosystems would not be adapted to the new environmental conditions, nor to the local contexts in which they are inserted. A paroxysmal example is the restoration of native ecosystems in urban contexts: Joshua Zeunert[93] uses this example to criticise restoration as it is currently practised. He looks at restoration in urban contexts in Australia and notes that it is often done in the same way as in rural contexts. In his view, the 'fashion' for restoration leads some states to adopt it as a systematic solution, regardless of the context, without thinking in depth about the *why* and the *how*. However, in many urban contexts, restoration simply seems unfeasible and unsuited to the social and economic issues at stake: natural entities requiring permanent care from humans risk not being integrated into the rhythm of the urban environment.

Furthermore, the historical state of reference is often chosen more for cultural than scientific reasons: it will be the state that evokes an idyllic nature for the greatest number of people. In Australia, for example, it is usually the pre-European landscape that is targeted, but at the same time separated from the Aboriginal impact that shaped it. In both the USA and Australia, restoration projects sometimes seem to revert to non-existent, supposedly wild, natural states where people were already having an impact. Even taking this impact into account, is it possible to reproduce an ecosystem that was interacting with a few hundred humans and will be interacting with thousands in the future? Stuart K. Allison, who has himself been involved in ecological restoration projects, outlines the classic obstacles encountered in restoration in the United States: in the case of Illinois - where the author conducted his experiments - the vast majority of restorations involve the transformation of agricultural land into tall grass prairies.[94] . This choice is not motivated by ecological but by historical reasons: since tall grasslands were the first ecosystem that settlers encountered, they occupy an important place in regional myths, expressing for many a point of origin of the local community. For these same historical reasons, restoration projects therefore target the grasslands as they were before European settlement. Yet, as Allison points out, very little is known about this natural period and and we have - at best - records of species that existed at the time; but no information on their distribution and proportions. Secondly, the majority of restoration projects are relatively small and can therefore not accommodate the large species that used to occupy these grasslands, such as bison. For other species such as grey wolves, no restoration project is able to provide the space necessary for their reintroduction. Third, because the grasslands of Illinois were already shaped by Native American fire prior to the arrival of settlers, restorationists face a dilemma: they can either maintain this fire practice, which is integral to the grasslands as we know them, but can no longer present restoration as a return to the wilderness, or they can decide to abandon this practice and risk failure of both the historic baseline and the project itself. For Allison, this type of project in Illinois is indicative of the difficulty of separating nature and culture in the continuum of a place. Restoration is easier in the United States than in Europe, Asia or Africa, given the even longer human impact on these continents.

Constance Pierce sums up this chimerical aspect of restoration as follows: 'What does restoration restore to us? certainly not the past. [...] nothing is restored. Something is presented with an eye to history.'[95] Restoration would therefore at best be 'reinvention,' never 'reproduction.' In studying prairie restorations, Pierce has come to the conclusion that they are primarily places of ritual, resulting from complex processes of selection and interpretation. This does not lead her to denigrate restoration as a practice, but rather to criticise the assumptions attached to it, including the very possibility of returning to a past natural state: 'to deny the laws of time is sheer madness.'[96] Indeed, if one decides to 'rehabilitate' an ecosystem and thus not turn it into an impenetrable natural area, is it realistic and relevant to return to a pre-human ecosystem? Even allowing for the continuous modification of ecosystems by various species, including human beings, the current explosion in population, its influence on nature and the resources it necessarily requires, raises questions about the capacity and sustainability of ancient ecosystems if they are restored.

Here again we come back to the dilemma of genesis and quality: is it better to have an ecosystem that is faithful to the past or one whose composition is adapted to the future? This second solution of course runs the risk of nature being thought of only in relation to the evolution of the human species and its needs, and not for the good of the ecosystem itself. However, rigorous knowledge of and respect for nature does not necessarily lead to considering an ecosystem that is thousands of years old as 'better:' this is also a form of anthropocentrism insofar as an ancient landscape is chosen because it is of great value in the collective imagination. For Zeunert, it is a misunderstanding of nature to claim that its past provides the best answers for its future. He argues that the retrospectivity of restoration is its main cause of failure, preventing its integration into the present environment and its resilience. Indeed, restoration, when practised in a traditional way, is a very important part of the process, responds to several assumptions that are, however, questionable:

1. The former state of an ecosystem is optimal for its current development.
2. The ecosystem was in a harmonious situation in the past, which can be found in the present environmental conditions.

3. The restored ecosystem will be able to grow in the future and be resilient to environmental changes.

These assumptions on which restoration is based are difficult to verify and certainly not adequate to all situations. Zeunert points out that this is a 'return to basics' that can be found in other contexts, a nostalgic paradigm that would have it that in nature as well as in culture, the former state was always better: nature would then have been tainted by humans and the only possible state of return would be that of pre-humanity. All foreign and non-native species would then have to be removed from the ecosystem.

The Dangers of a Static View of Ecosystems in Restoration

This risk of 'purifying' nature to the detriment of its respect has been identified by thinkers in philosophy as well as in the life sciences; it seems particularly present in restoration given its strong relationship with the past. An article published in 2011 by Mark Davis and eighteen other ecologists in the journal *Nature*[97] had a strong echo among environmental thinkers: the authors denounced the obsession with the origin of species in current environmental practice. They argue that conservationists, restorationists and other environmentalists have focused too much on the nativity of species rather than their environmental impact, leading to less effective policies:

> It is time for scientists, land managers and policy makers to abandon their obsession

with the native/foreign dichotomy, and
adopt more dynamic and pragmatic approaches to species conservation and management - approaches more appropriate to
our rapidly changing planet.[98]

The eighteen authors consider it pure ideology
to judge an ecosystem according to the origin of
the species present in it, whereas practically all
ecosystems are made up of old and new species,
and these movements, even if they are sometimes
harmful, are not intrinsically bad for nature; it is
therefore irrelevant to look for a 'good historical
state.' It is a question of observing what species
do, not where they come from: if they have a
positive impact on biodiversity, on the regulation
and health of the ecosystem, etc., then, by these
criteria, native species can be just as good or bad
as non-native species. It follows that the advocates of future-oriented restoration fall in line
with this critique. Joshua Zeunert argues that
past biodiversity is not inherently better than
present biodiversity, despite species movements,
environmental changes, or some animals having
adapted to new habitats as well as to their native habitat. Young D. Choi, another advocate of
future restoration, offers the analogy of restored
nature and a prosthesis on a leg: the purpose
of a prosthesis is not to recompose the original
flesh and bone, but to rehabilitate the original
function; for Choi, therefore, it is not the composition of the 'materials' used that counts, but
the restoration of function within the whole, as
the prosthesis does for the human body, and the
restored entity within an ecosystem. Joshua Zeunert and Young D. Choi, therefore, character-
ise classical restoration as prescriptive, inflexible,
dogmatic, past-oriented, static and idealistic.

The Restoration Paradigm of the Future

The paradigm shift is summarised by Young D. Choi as follows: 'our ecological restoration paradigm must be redefined by functional rehabilitations for the future, not by nostalgic recompositions of the past.' [99] Restoration that looks to the past would thus be both ineffective and based more on ideology than on the real needs of nature. Young D. Choi adds another criticism to this paradigm of the past: too much fidelity to the past prevents the ecosystem from allowing for the independence and unpredictability that is essential (the potential for autonomy). Thus, for Choi, it is necessary to foresee a multiplicity of trajectories for a restoration project. Hyperfidelity to the past would risk foreseeing the past as the end point of the trajectory, whereas the human-restored state should only be a starting point. The end point of a restoration should not be predictable. Joshua Zeunert supports this idea by proposing the concept of landscape flexibility: 'It is imperative that the landscapes we create are flexible and multifunctional.' [100] Indeed, ecosystems must be able to adapt to various evolutionary scenarios, containing a high probability of human population growth and resource scarcity.

On the other hand, loyalty to the past creates the risk of forgetting the human activities that shaped the landscape. Indeed, as has been observed in the Netherlands, restoration projects on land that has been directly modified by humans - through agriculture, industry, or indigenous practices of fire, hunting and gathering - can easily be experienced as a denial of identity. For those who shaped the land, the history of that activity and its traces are of great value. Often, restoration thus implies erasing from the history of a place several decades or centuries of practices. This is a very strong political choice, which must be decided democratically by the community interacting with the place. The issues are not the same in different regions: while in the United States and Australia a return to wilderness often excludes from history the interactions that indigenous populations have had with the ecosystem, in Europe it is the question of the industrial past of certain places that seems to be the most sensitive. European restoration projects have in fact sometimes concerned post-industrial sites, notably former mines or factory sites. Any erasure of traces of history must be debated, balancing the value of nature and that of human cultures, in order to achieve a restoration that is in keeping with the 'sense of place' and is accepted locally.

The Characteristics of a Restoration of the Future

Based on this new paradigm, a future-oriented restoration should:

1. Establish ecosystems that extend into the future rather than the past: flexible and resilient ecosystems.
2. Focus on the rehabilitation of ecosystem functions rather than on the recomposition of native species.
3. Offer alternative trajectories for the ecosystem, and no fixed end point.
4. Integrate the human history of the site into the restoration process.

5.
"We Need To Cultivate Our Garden:" The Return to a Simple Interaction With Nature

'This is well said, replied Candide, but we must cultivate our garden:'[101] the famous prescription uttered by Candide at the end of Voltaire's tale takes us back to the basics of the relationship with nature. Any good act of restoration implies a reinvention of the individual's relationship with the nature that surrounds him or her. In this sense, the simple fact of immersing oneself in the study of a forest, a meadow or a plant in order to rehabilitate it is at the same time always a way of questioning oneself, of cultivating one's spirit. The act of restoration is also in line with another interpretation of Voltaire's dictum: the refusal of fatalism and its replacement by an optimistic faith in a human species capable of improving its condition. Any restoration project is ultimately a refusal of environmental fatalism, a belief that each human can repair some of what humanity as a whole has destroyed, without any particular scientific skills. It is also about remembering that the garden is an ancient and assimi-

lated form of natural artefact, which has allowed
for simple relationships between humans and
nature, also marked by human creation and design. is restoration not then an evolved form of
gardening? this is the theory of Stuart K. Allison: the author sees restoration as too big a word
for spontaneous and inclusive action. For him,
'restoration' applies to cars or works of art, but
seems too mechanical and complex for the rehabilitation of ecosystems. He therefore prefers
the term 'gardening,' which emphasises the personal relationship between humans and nature.
Although gardening[102] easily evokes the prospect
of a highly artificial and controlled nature, it also
expresses the human care for a piece of nature,
the 'belief in the seed.' Thus Allison is inspired by
Aldo Leopold's vision of restoration, for whom it
was better for the 'average farm boy'[103] to take
an interest in the pine trees in his farmyard than
for restoration to become an academic discipline
monopolised by experts. Moreover, like restored
nature, a garden is - mostly - emancipated from
the design humans have planned for it. In this,
Allison sees restoration as the most advanced
form of gardening, the simple return to the land:

> To restore the human connection to the
> earth, we need to return to a small-scale,
> personal relationship with the environ-
> ment, like a kneeling gardener planting
> bulbs in fresh autumn soil. [104]

conclusion

'By restoring life to things, I want to celebrate the creativity of what Klee called *form making*.' [105] Referring to Paul Klee - for whom form making is life, as opposed to form being only death - Tim Ingold makes a strong appeal to go beyond the idea of an agent-imposed form on passive and inert matter. 'Restoring life to things' means moving from a static entity based on the role of an agent to a moving entity based on the fact that it is alive. In the same sense, ecological restoration should not be seen as a pale copy of the past, but as a creative act, allowing life to be reinserted into an ecosystem. By relying on both biomimetics and human practices and technology, the restorer creates a unique situation of hybridity and an opportunity to re-inhabit the environment. Tim Ingold calls this the shift from 'object' to 'thing:' the thing consists of flows and transformations rather than states of matter. Thus, what differentiates the tree-thing from the tree-object is its connection to the wind moving its leaves, to the insects occupying its trunk, its permanent interaction with other entities: 'the tree is not an object at all, but a certain gathering of all the networks of life.' [106] Restoration, as a creation of form, must indeed become a 'weaving' of nature, an interaction between natural materials on the one hand and adaptive human thinking on the other, in which the design of the ecosystem is not fixed in advance. It is this approach that will enable 'good ecological restoration.'

This paradigm can be found in the study of all natural artefacts: just as the relationship to the past cannot be the only criterion for the success of a restoration, or even its main threat, no natural artefact deserves to be a mere static reproduction of form. The natural artefact should be

neither the material creation of a design existing in human thought, nor the reproduction of
a natural form. In this sense, all natural artefact
production is creative biomimetics. Only in this
way can the world be inhabited and not occupied, and this reasoning applies equally to natural and artificial things. Whereas in an occupied
world objects appear to be already locked in their
final form, inhabiting the world means joining
a continuous process of formation. The creator
of natural artefacts thus becomes an alchemist,
working with materials without always knowing
what form he will arrive at.

Four principles can be distinguished to qualify
'good natural artefacts' from these reflections:

1. The principle of ecopoiesis: the good natural
   artefact tends towards ecopoiesis, the art of
   making the world habitable for all present
   and future living things.
2. The principle of democracy: the production
   of a good natural artefact is subject to democratic negotiation and debate with the living
   entities involved in its existence.
3. The principle of dynamism: the good natural
   artefact is part of a dynamic conception of
   ecosystem evolution, aiming at sustainability
   and resilience rather than the identical reproduction of past or present entities.
4. The principle of dual benefit: the right natural artefact serves a natural ecosystem as much
   as it allows human communities to connect
   with and learn from nature.

The simple theoretical recognition of the concept
of natural artefacts allows us to move beyond the
vision of humans outside nature that has pre-

vailed for too long, both on the side of the eco-logical advocates and the indifferent. Good natural artefacts offer hope for reversing the threat of technique described by Hans Jonas.

Beyond their theoretical recognition and ethical inclusion, natural artefacts need to enter public debate. At the community level, the creation of a natural artefact must necessarily be accompanied by a democratic process

This is a process that allows the definition of the contours of this new commons which becomes the receptacle of cultural heritages. The launch of a restoration project is indeed an opportunity to reflect on what makes up the identity of a territory and on the relations that the community wishes to maintain with its environment; in this respect, this process is eminently political and must be treated as such. This is also why it must go beyond simple community debate: the status and production of natural artefacts merit major citizen debates such as those that have arisen around certain bioethical issues. It is, in fact, a question of reflecting on the new hybrid objects that a state wishes to include in its democracy, whose interests it wishes to take into account.

The debate on this subject is particularly weak in Europe, whereas in the United States it has always been of some importance to both professionals and non-professionals. The existing literature on restoration is almost exclusively American, Canadian and Australian. This discrepancy can be explained by the political and historical importance of the wilderness in these three countries, particularly in relation to the colonisation of the land and the treatment of the native population. The so-called 'myth of the frontier'[107] has created a particular sensitivity to the loss, creation and restoration of wilderness. This political sensitivity is an opportunity for debate, but at the same time it sometimes creates distortions, leading one community, for example, to insist on a return to a particular time period that has strong cultural significance. When nostalgia for an idealised era takes precedence over the desire to restore a natural ecosystem, then restoration starts off on the wrong foot.

In Europe, the debate is sufficiently insensitive to invent a suitable form of democracy and to experiment with new practices of common ecology. Rare debates take place about large-scale natural artefacts. The massive urbanisation of the world is finally creating, perhaps unexpectedly, the most vivid places for debate about natural artefacts. The sheer size of metropolitan areas obliges us to introduce nature into them *en masse*, taking over every possible space - rooftops, basements, riverbanks, etc. Some built-up areas should be destroyed or left uncultivated *deliberately to bring nature in*. The emergence and re-definition of nature in the city all over the world is an opportunity to raise awareness and create proper democratic debate. The small scale of urban natural artefacts should not overshadow the need for large-scale natural area restoration and conservation projects, but it does provide opportunities for positive interactions and re-learning of environmental connections.

In this framework, which is very different from that of the wilderness, the question is less that of human intervention in nature than that of the incursion of nature into the city, in a territory that has lived under the illusion of human autonomy. The recognition of natural artefacts therefore necessarily leads to an in-depth transformation not only of ecology and politics, but also of the way in which space is made, and therefore of architecture, urbanism and landscaping. The need for reinhabitation concerns natural spaces as much as those massively invested by human beings and brings to light a certain number of urgent issues: human buildings can no longer be designed independently of the buildings of other living beings; any new construction must make the world more habitable, beyond the individuals who will occupy it; cities must be spaces for the coexistence of species, and should be planned as such. Finally, no space, whether predominantly human or non-human, deserves to exclude the possibility of its inhabitability by other species or to confine them to the simple role of observer.

endnotes

1. Jacques Monod, *Le Hasard et la Nécessité* (Seuil, 1970), in Tim Ingold, 'Making Culture and Weaving the World,' in Sandra H. Dudley, *Museum Objects : Experiencing the Properties of Things*, Routledge, 2012.

2. Tim Ingold, 'Making Culture and Weaving the World,' in Sandra H. Dudley, *Museum Objects : Experiencing the Properties of Things*, Routledge, 2012.

3. Tim Ingold, 'Making Culture and Weaving the World,' art. cit.

4. Aristotle, *Physics*, book II, chapter 1.

5. Risto Hilpinen, 'artifact,' *Stanford Encyclopedia of Philosophy*, 2004.

6. Gilles Kassel, ''Vers une ontologie formelle des artefacts,' in *Actes d'IC*, PUG, Grenoble, 2009.

7. Helena Siipi, 'Artefacts and Living Artefacts,' *Environmental Values 12*, 2003, p. 413-30.

8. Roland Schaer, *Répondre du Vivant*, Paris, le Pommier, 2013.

9. Thomas H. Birch, 'The Incarceration of Wildness: Wilderness areas as Prisons,' *Environmental Ethics*, Vol. 12, 1990, Center for Environmental Philosophy, University of North Texas, trad. Hicham-Stéphane Afeissa, in *Éthique de l'Environnement*, Paris, Vrin, 2007.

10. 'Wilderness' also in the original French text, a term difficult to translate, taken to express savagery, purity through the non-intervention of the human.

11. Especially J. B. CallIcott, Helena SiipI, op. cit., et Ben Cullen, 'Living Artefact, Personal Ecosystem, Biocultural Schizophrenia: a Novel Synthesis of Processual and Post-processual Thinking,' *Proceedings of the Prehistoric Society*, Vol. 61, 1995, p. 371-391.

12. 'Façonné' in the French text, implying crafting rather than the term used here, 'designed.'

13. John Baird CallIicott, 'Animal Liberation: a Triangular Affair,' in C. Pierce et D. Van De Veer (eds), *People, Penguins, and Plastic Trees*, Belmont: Wadsworth Publishing company, 1995, p. 237-254.

14. Éric Katz, 'Artefacts and Functions: a note on the Value of Nature,' *Environmental Values* 2 (1993), p. 223-32.

15. Ibid.

16. Yeuk-Sze Lo, 'Natural and Artifactual: Restored Nature as Subject,' *Environmental Ethics,* Vol. 21, 1999.

17. Éric Katz, 'Artefacts and Functions: a note on the Value of Nature,' *Environmental Values* 2 (1993), p. 223-32.

18. Ibid.

19. Aldo Leopold, 'Wilderness as a Form of Land Use,' *The Journal of Land & Public Utility Economics*, Vol.1, n° 4, 1925, p. 398-404.

20. In Thomas H. Birch, 'The Incarceration of Wildness: Wilderness Areas as Prisons,' *Environmental Ethics*, vol. 12, 1990, trans. Hicham-Stéphane Afeissa in Éthique de l'Environnement, cit.

21. Aldo Leopold, *Almanach d'un Comté des Sables*, trans. Anna Gibson, Paris, Flammarion, 2000.

22. Éric Katz, 'Artefacts and Functions: a note on the Value of Nature,' *Environmental Values* 2 (1993), p. 223-32.

23. In Thomas H. Birch, 'The Incarceration of Wildness: Wilderness Areas as Prisons,' cit.

24. Bruno Latour, *Nous N'avons Jamais Été Modernes,* Paris, la Découverte, 1991.

25. Arne Naess, 'The Shallow and the Deep, Long-range Ecology Movement, a Summary,' Inquiry, vol. 16, 1973. trans. H.-S. Afeissa in *Éthique de l'Environnement*, cit.

26. Bruno Latour uses the term 'non-humans' lacking a better notion, judging it himself 'not great.' He wishes to avoid the nature - society dichotomy, as well as that of subject - object. 'Non-humans' has the merit -in Latour's view- of underlining the links between humans and those on whom they depend to exist.

27. Bruno Latour, *Nous n'Avons Jamais Été Modernes,* Paris, la Découverte, 1991.

28. Ibid.

29. Michael E. Soule, Gary Lease, *Reinventing Nature? Responses to Postmodern Deconstruction*, Island Press, 1995.

30. Katherine Hayles, 'Searching for Common Ground,' in Michael E. Soule, Gary Lease, *Reinventing Nature? Responses to Postmodern Deconstruction*, cit.

31. Michael E. Soule, 'The Social Siege of Nature,' in Michael E. Soule, Gary Lease, *Reinventing Nature? Responses to Postmodern Deconstruction*, cit.

32. Albert Borgmann, 'The Nature of Reality and the Reality of Nature,' in Michael E. Soule, Gary Lease, *Reinventing Nature? Responses to Postmodern Deconstruction*, cit.

33. United Nations, *Rio Declaration on Environment and Development*, Principle 7, 1992.

34. Nathalie Blanc and Jacques Lolive nonetheless underline in their text 'La Restauration Ecologique: une Nouvelle Formation du Monde?' (*Cybergeo : European Journal of Geography* [online], Dossiers, Esthétique et Environnement, document 479, 2009) that the debate is beginning to develop in France, particularly through the creation of the group 'Restoration Ecologique' in the Functional Ecology Centre of Montpellier University.

35. Bi-monthly review published by Wiley Periodicals, Inc.

36. Quadrennial review published by University of Wisconsin Press.

37. Triennial review published by Wiley Blackwell.

38. Society for Ecological Restoration, 1990.

39. Society for Ecological Restoration, 1995.

40. Definition given by the Science and Policy Working Group, SER, 2002.

41. Hein-Anton Van Der Heijden, 'Ecological Restoration, Environmentalism and the Dutch Politics of 'New Nature,'' *Environmental Values* 14, 2005, p. 427-46.

42. Frederick Turner, 'The Invented Landscape,' in A. D. Baldwin Jr., J. De Luce, & C. Pletsch (eds.), *Beyond Preservation: Restoring and Inventing Landscape*, Minneapolis, University of Minnesota Press, 1994, p. 35-66 et p. 251-259.

43. The New Nature Movement is particularly present in Holland.

44. This typology is particularly presented by Swart, Van Der Windt et Keulartz in 'Valuation of Nature in Conservation and Restoration,' *Restoration Ecology*, vol. 9/2, 2001, p. 230-238.

45. Helena Siipi, 'Artefacts and Living Artefacts,' cit.

46. Eric Katz, 'Nature's Presence: Reflections on Healing and Domination,' *Philosophy and Geography* 1, 1996, p. 197.

47. Robert Elliot, 'Faking Nature,' *Inquiry*, 25 (1), 1982, p. 81.

48. Eric Katz, 'The Big Lie: Human Restoration of Nature,' *Research in Philosophy and Technology*, vol. 12, 1992, trans. Hicham-Stéphane Afeïssa in Éthique de l'Environnement, cit.

49. Jacqueline LichensteIn, 'Disegno,' in *Vocabulaire Europ*éen des Philosophies, Dictionnaire des Intraduisibles, dir. Barbara Cassin, Paris, le Seuil / Dictionnaires le Robert, 2004.

50. Giorgio Vasari, *Le Vite de' Più Eccellenti Pittori, Scultori e Architettori*, Florence, 1568, cited in Jacqueline Lichenstein, 'Disegno,' op. cit.

51. Holly Jones, Oswald Schmitz, 'Rapid Recovery of Damaged Ecosystems,' PLoS ONE 4 (5) : 2009, p. 1-6, in Joshua Zeunert, 'Challenging Assumptions in Urban Restoration Ecology,' *Landscape Journal* 32 : 2, 2013.

52. Margaret Palmer, 'Reforming Watershed Restoration: Science in Need of Application and Applications in Need of Science,' *Estuaries Coasts* 32 (1): 2009, p. 1-6,

in Joshua Zeunert, 'Challenging Assumptions in Urban Restoration Ecology,' cit.

53. Robert Elliot, 'Faking Nature,' op. cit.

54. Chris Maser, *The Redesigned Forest*, R. and E. Miles, 1988.

55. Ibid.

56. Chris Maser, *The Redesigned Forest*, cit.

57. Ibid.

58. Frederick Rurner, The Invented Landscape, in A. D. Baldwin Jr., J. De Luce, & C. Pletsch (eds.), *Beyond Preservation: Restoring and Inventing Landscape*, cit., p. 35-66 and 251-259.

59. 'Wilderness Act,' 1964.

60. W. Throop, *Environmental Restoration: Ethics, Theory and Practice*, Amherst, NY, Humanity Books, 2000, in Robert l. Chapman, 'Ecological Restoration Restored,' *Environmental Values* 15, 2006.

61. Henry David Thoreau, 'Walking,' *Atlantic Monthly,* 1862.

62. Aldo Leopold, *A Sand County Almanach*, New York, Oxford University Press, 1970, in Robert L. Chapman, 'Ecological Restoration Restored,' *Environmental Values 15*, 2006.

63. Aldo Leopold, *The River of the Mother of God and Other Essays by Aldo Leopold*, ed. Susan L. Flader, J. Baird Calllcott, Madison, University of Wisconsin Press, 1991, in Robert L. Chapman, 'Ecological Restoration Restored, Environmental Values,' cit.

64. Robert L. Chapman, 'Ecological Restoration Restored, Environmental Values,' cit.

65. Hans Jonas, *Le Principe Responsabilité*, trans. Jean Greisch, Paris, Flammarion, 2008.

66. Ibid., p. 40.

67. Hans Jonas, *Pour Une Ethique du Futur*, Rivages, 1998, p. 108.

68. Stephanie Mills, *In Service of the Wild*, Boston, Beacon Press, 1995.

69. These include a grassland project in Illinois, a wild salmon reintroduction project in the Pacific, and the Auroville restoration project in India.

70. Ibid.

71. Donna Ladkin, 'Does 'Restoration' Necessarily Imply the Domination of Nature?,' *Environmental Values* 14, 2005, p. 203-19.

72. Stephanie Mills, *In Service of the Wild*, cit.

73. Benjamin Hale, Remediation and Respect: Do Remediation Technologies Alter Our Responsibility?,' *Environmental Values* 18, 2009, p. 397-415.

74. Idem.

75. Ibid.

76. Swart, Van Der Windt and Keulartz in 'Valuation of Nature in Conservation and Restoration,' *Restoration Ecology*, Vol. 9, n°2, 2001, p. 230-238.

77. Donna Ladkin, Does 'Restoration' Necessarily Imply the Domination of Nature?,' *Environmental Values* 14, 2005, p. 203-19.

78. Richard Sylvan, 'Mucking with Nature,' unpublished article, 1992 in Donna Ladkin, 'Does 'Restoration' Necessarily Imply the Domination of Nature?,' cit.

79. Peter Berg, Raymond F. DasMann, 'Reinhabiting California' in Peter Berg, *Reinhabiting a Separate Country: a Bioregional Anthology of Northern California*, in Stephanie Mills, *In Service of the Wild*, cit.

80. Stephanie Mills, *In Service of the Wild* cit.

81. Stephanie Mills, *In Service of the Wild* cit.

82. Matthias Gross, 'Classical Sociology and the Restoration of Nature: the Relevance of Emile Durkheim and Georg Simmel,' *Organization Environment*, 13, 2000, p. 277.

83. Ibid.

84. Eric Higgs, 'The Two-Culture Problem: Ecological Restoration and the Integration of Knowledge,' *Restoration Ecology*, Vol. 13, n° 1, 159, p. 159-164.

85. Eric Higgs, 'What is Good Ecological Restoration?,' *Conservation Biology*, Vol. 11, n° 2, 1997, p. 338-348.

86. John Cairns, 'Ecosocietal Restoration: Reestablishing Humanity's Relationship with Natural Systems,' *Environment*, Vol. 37, 1995 p. 4-33.

87. Eric Higgs, 'What is Good Ecological Restoration?,' cit.

88. William Jordan III, 'Sunflower Forest : Ecological Restoration as the Basis for a New Environmental Paradigm,' in A.D. Baldwin Jr., J. De Luce & C. Pletsch (eds.), *Beyond Preservation: Restoring and Inventing Landscape*, cit., p. 35-66 et 251-259.

89. Andrew Light, Eric S. Higgs, 'The Politics of Ecological Restoration,' *Environmental Ethics*, Vol. 18, 1996.

90. Light and Higgs cite in particular the example of the prairie restoration undertaken by IBM near Minneapolis.

91. Andrew Light, 'Restoration, the Value of Participation, and the Risks of Professionalization,' in Paul H. Gobster, R. Bruce Hull, *Restoring Nature, Perspectives from the Social Sciences and Humanities*, Island Press, 2000.

92. Stuart K. Allison, 'What Do We Mean When We talk About Ecological Restoration?,' *Ecological Restoration,* Vol. 22, n° 4, 2004.

93. Joshua Zeunert, 'Challenging Assumptions in Urban Restoration Ecology,' *Landscape Journal*, Vol. 32, n° 2, 2013.

94. Stuart K. Allison, 'What Do We Mean When We talk About Ecological Restoration?,' *Ecological Restoration,* cit.

95. Constance Pierce, 'The Poetics and Politics of Prairie Restoration,' in A. D. BaldwIn Jr., J. De Luce & C. Pletsch (eds.), *Beyond Preservation : Restoring and Inventing Landscape*, cit., p. 35-66 et 251-259.

96. Ibid.

97. Mark A. Davis et al., 'Don't Judge species on their origins,' *Nature*, Vol. 474, 2011.

98. Ibid.

99. Young D. Choi, 'Restoration Ecology to the Future: A Call for New Paradigm,' *Restoration Ecology*, Vol. 15, n° 2, 2007, p. 351-353.

100. Joshua Zeunert, 'Challenging Assumptions in Urban Restoration Ecology,' cit.

101. Voltaire, *Candide ou l'Optimisme,* Chapter 30.

102. Stuart K. Allison, 'What Do We Mean When We talk About Ecological Restoration?,' *Ecological Restoration,* cit.

103. Ibid.

104. Ibid.

105. Tim Ingold, 'Bringing things Back to Life: Creative Entanglements in a World of Materials,' *NCRM Working Paper.* Realities / Morgan Centre, University of Manchester, 2010 (unpublished).

106. Ibid.

107. The 'frontier myth' refers to the limit of settlement accomplished by European colonists during the 'conquest of the west.'